FLORENCE NIGHTINGALE
AND THE DOCTORS

Miss Florence Nightingale.
at Embley.
December 28 th 1857.

Florence Nightingale, aged thirty-seven

(From a portrait, now in the National Portrait Gallery, by Sir George Scharf, one of the first Directors of the National Portrait Gallery)

ZACHARY COPE

Florence Nightingale
and
The Doctors

J. B. LIPPINCOTT COMPANY
Philadelphia and Montreal

First Published by the Museum Press Ltd.
26 Old Brompton Road, London, S.W.7
1958

Published and distributed in North America
for the Museum Press Ltd. by
J. B. Lippincott Company

PRINTED IN GREAT BRITAIN BY
SPOTTISWOODE, BALLANTYNE & CO. LTD.
LONDON AND COLCHESTER
(R. 3161)

Preface

Florence Nightingale devoted most of her long life to the service of medicine, and necessarily corresponded or came into contact with many of the leaders of the medical profession. A study of the voluminous material now available serves to show how great her influence was, and at the same time makes it clear that she was greatly helped by the doctors with whom she collaborated.

A few of the letters printed in this book have already appeared in one or other of the excellent biographies of Miss Nightingale, but most of the extracts have never to our knowledge previously been printed. It is hoped that this brief account may help to elucidate the complex character of this most distinguished woman of the Victorian era.

ZACHARY COPE

Acknowledgements

I wish to express my thanks to the authorities of the British Museum Library and of the Bodleian Library for allowing me access to the Nightingale manuscripts and letters in their possession; to Sir Maurice Bonham Carter for granting me permission to publish extracts from the letters of Miss Nightingale; and to Sir William Acland, Bt., for allowing me to publish letters written by his father, the late Sir Henry Wentworth Acland, Bt. I am grateful to Lieutenant-General W. A. D. Drummond, Director-General of the Army Medical Service, for calling my attention to, and permitting me to publish the letters written from Scutari by Dr Gregg; and to Major-General Hilton-Sergeant, Commandant of the R.A.M.C. College, Millbank, for allowing me access to documents in the library of the College.

I have received welcome help from Miss E. M. McInnes, archivist to St Thomas's Hospital; from Mr Wade, Librarian of the Royal Society of Medicine; and from Mr Davies, Librarian of the R.A.M.C. College Library. I am indebted to Dr Ashworth Underwood, Director of the Wellcome Museum, for help given by the photographic department of that Museum; I have received similar help from the photographic department of the Royal Society of Medicine. My thanks are due to the editors and proprietors of the *Illustrated London News* and of the *Sphere* for permission to reproduce illustrations which first appeared in those journals. The source of other illustrations, when obtainable, is given in the text.

I am indebted for certain information to *The Life of Sir John Hall*, by S. M. Mitra (Longmans, Green and Co), to *The Life of Sir John McNeill* (published by John Murray), and to *The Child of Destiny*, by Ishbel Ross (publisher Israel Gollancz).

Finally I am very grateful to my friend Dr Maurice Davidson for reading through the manuscript and for giving me several valuable suggestions.

Z. C.

Contents

Illustrations

I

Miss Nightingale's general attitude towards Doctors

IN A LETTER written to her cousin, Miss Hilary Bonham Carter, dated 8 January 1852, Miss Nightingale commented: 'I can always talk better to a medical man than to any one else. They have not that detestable nationality which makes it so difficult to talk with an Englishman. I suppose the habit of examining organizations gives them this.'

From this comment one is encouraged to think that by a study of her relations with doctors it may be possible to obtain a truer picture of her character than by other lines of investigation. At nearly every stage of her public life she came into contact with doctors, and among them were many of her best friends. Her life-work had much in common with the work of medical men, and she herself had an important influence on certain aspects of medicine, particularly preventive medicine. She was a great sanitarian, an earnest advocate of fresh air, pure water and good drainage. She took a great interest in the construction of hospitals, and for half a century her advice was sought by most of those who were planning large hospitals in all parts of the English-speaking world. Mainly by her efforts the Army Medical College was founded, and her work in connection with the Sanitary Commission of 1857 led to a great improvement in the general health and conditions in the Army. With the help of Dr Farr she made a brave attempt to put the classification of diseases on a surer foundation and to institute a uniform system of hospital statistics.

Though few famous persons have been more fortunate in their biographers, it may be possible to see some extra facets of her complex character by examining more closely her attitude towards the medical profession and her relationship to individual doctors.

For this purpose we depend for our material largely upon letters written to Miss Nightingale by doctors and, even more important, letters written to those doctors by Miss Nightingale. In this connection it must be made clear that there were two distinct aspects to her personality. One, which she presented to the public and to those to whom she granted personal interviews, was that of the discreet, diplomatic, tactful person, anxious to obtain information and careful not to arouse animosities. This same aspect is seen in nearly all her official communications. The other aspect of her personality was that which she revealed to her close friends, persons whom she could absolutely trust not to let her confidential and sometimes indiscreet remarks go further. In such communications she had few if any inhibitions, and made remarks some of which it would be unwise or uncharitable to publish. Frequently she asked her friends either to burn her letters or return them, and in one instance she wrote a letter to Dr (afterwards Sir William) Bowman, in which, in different parts, she asked him both to burn it and return it. In all her intimate correspondence we see the first impulsive outburst of an active mind, which would undoubtedly have been consideredly modified on more mature consideration.

A study of Miss Nightingale's correspondence enables one to obtain a clearer view of the general state of medicine in the mid-Victorian era, and to realize the great influence she exerted upon it. It may be asked why her influence in this direction has been so little recognized. The answer is simple. She purposely kept in the background, and pursued her plans by means of private and confidential communications and interviews, the reports of which were enshrined in her own or other people's private papers. Some of these papers have only recently become accessible. Moreover, her invalid or semi-invalid state, which lasted more than half her life, but did not affect her mental or epistolary activity, enabled her easily and naturally to concentrate on the matters in which she was interested, and compelled those who wished to ask her advice to seek a personal interview. At these interviews she was accustomed to extract all possible information out of her visitor and to make copious notes, volumes of which have been carefully preserved. So effectually did she conceal her identity and hide her activities that she is not so much as mentioned in the accounts of the lives of Dr John Sutherland and Dr William Farr in the *Dictionary of National Biography*. Yet for thirty years she worked in close collaboration with the former and for twenty years collaborated in important statistical calculations with the latter. Miss Nightingale was always willing to help enquirers by giving the results of her own experience, but she was unwilling to appear to give advice and often marked her letters 'Private'. This diffidence sometimes put those who consulted her in some difficulty. When Dr Ogle, physician to the Derby Royal Infirmary, wrote to her asking her advice and inviting her to become patroness of the new Nursing Association which was being formed, Miss Nightingale replied—

> I must clearly be considered as merely aiding you because I am asked and the reason you will see at once is that I must not even in appearance interfere with the entire liberty of judgement and action on the part of your committee and association. For the same reason I should not like my opinion to be cited to influence any one's judgement. I wish to inform all sides and to take part with none, but only to give all sides the means of forming a judgement. You will see that it would transgress this rule were I to become a patroness of your nursing association.

This limitation put Dr Ogle in some difficulty. He replied—

> The only thing that I must at least put before you is the difficulty in which I am placed by the word 'Private' which seems to debar me from making use of your hints. I can hardly expect either the Governors of the Infirmary or the members of the Nursing Association to listen to me unless I can support my recommendation by an appeal to experience. To be able to say that you have found this and that productive of 'great mischief' would be enough but without some such authority I should seem to be merely advancing one theory in place of another, and the apparent instability of purpose would shake the confidence of the Public in the whole movement.

It is clear that Dr Ogle took his instructions too literally.

Some of Miss Nightingale's views on medicine were many years ahead of her time, some conformed to the medical doctrine then current, but in a few important points she did not keep up with progress of contemporary scientific medical knowledge. In the matter of sanitation she was well ahead of her time, as she was also in appreciating the value of fresh air, a regular life, and graduated exercise in the treatment of pulmonary tuberculosis. She estimated the value of the ordinary 'bottle of medicine' correctly. When she was most busy with her public work the 'germ' theory of disease was in its infancy. Few microbic causes of disease had been identified and there were still educated and prominent doctors who did not accept the new teaching. Moreover, though the importance of improved sanitary measures had been strongly advocated by Chadwick and others, the bulk of the medical profession were slow to appreciate how great a reformation was needed. There was little scientific method either in diagnosis or treatment, and all the practising doctor could do was to help the natural cure by general measures. In her *Notes on Nursing*, published in 1859, Miss Nightingale was voicing the general view when she wrote concerning the treatment of fever—

> In these and many other similar diseases the exact value of particular remedies and modes of treatment is by no means ascertained, while there is universal experience as to the extreme importance of careful nursing in determining the issue of the disease.

At a time when many people believed in the spontaneous origin of living organisms it was not so surprising for anyone to teach, as Miss Nightingale did, that many fevers were not contagious but arose spontaneously as the result of accumulated filth. She did not believe in 'infection' or 'contagion', as may be judged by this curious passage culled from her *Notes on Nursing*—

> I was brought up, both by scientific men and ignorant women, distinctly to believe that small-pox, for instance, was a thing of which there was once a first specimen in the world, which went on propagating itself, in a perpetual chain of descent, just as much as that there was a first dog (or pair of dogs) and that small-pox would not begin itself any more than a new dog would begin without there having been a parent dog. Since then I have seen with my eyes and smelt

with my nose small-pox growing up in first specimens, either in close rooms or in overcrowded wards where it could not by any possibility have been 'caught' but must have begun. Nay more, I have seen diseases begin, grow up, and pass into one another. Now dogs do not pass into cats. I have seen for instance with a little overcrowding continued fever grow up; and with a little more, typhoid fever; and with a little more typhus, and all in the same ward or hut.

It is necessary to emphasize these rather curious views of Miss Nightingale, for they inspired her sanitary work, and they explain her strong antagonism to methods other than those she supported. It took the medical profession many years to understand and fully accept the 'germ' theory, and it is not surprising that Miss Nightingale never accepted it, particularly as her medical colleague, Dr Sutherland, was also conservative towards the new ideas. When she believed in anything she always did so wholeheartedly. On 6 November 1858 she wrote to Chadwick—

> Sanitary experience has so completely disproved the invisible 'seminal' contagions that I can only see a mania for being wrong in such letters as Greenhow's and Simon's. I never knew a case of infection, but there was gross mismanagement and carelessness.

It can be imagined therefore how puzzled and worried Miss Nightingale was when in 1873, in the newly built St Thomas's Hospital in which there were the latest sanitary devices, there occurred a serious outbreak of pyaemia. Her opposition to the theory of contagion and to the need for quarantine was expressed in a letter which she wrote to Dr Farr in 1861—

> I only modestly and really humbly say that I never saw a fact adduced in favour of contagion that would bear scientific enquiry, and I could name to you men whom you would acknowledge as scientific who place contagion on the same footing as witchcraft and other superstitions.

Her close colleague Dr Sutherland called contagion 'a London invention' and criticized Dr Farr for accepting Dr Snow's demonstration of the fact that cholera could be conveyed by water: 'You will find him reiterating again Dr Snow's fallacy about the destruction of the propagating fluid of cholera.' Snow was of course perfectly right in his contention, but Sutherland and his famous colleague could not or would not accept his demonstration as proof.

It was one of the contradictions in Miss Nightingale's way of thinking that she was most dogmatic in condemning the dogmas of the doctors. Though she had undergone no scientific training and, apart from the study of statistics, had no knowledge of scientific method, she condemned wholeheartedly the methods and results of scientists. In a letter to Dr Pattison Walker, written on 10 April 1866, she commented—

> I am afraid that you will think I am going beyond my province—but then you know you need not listen to what I say—if I say facts are everything, doctrines nothing. See what harm the German pathologists have done us. There are no specific diseases, there are specific disease conditions. It is that which is bringing the profession to grief and will in time work a great reform, to wit, to make them make the public care for its own health, and not rely on doctrine. It is a great thing for weak minds—the doctrine of contagion. The specific disease doctrine is the grand refuge of weak uncultured minds, such as now rule the medical profession from Dr Watson downwards—Watson who has the biggest practice in London. Pardon me these unprofessional words.

In spite of the mounting proof of the truth of bacterial infection Miss Nightingale would not be convinced. A legacy which she had put in her will for the purposes of founding a lectureship or professorship of statistics was revoked when she was over seventy years of age on the ground that she feared it might be used 'to endow some bacillus or microbe.'

Though she had not a high opinion of the curative power of medicine, she was always loyal to the doctors with whom she worked. Three months after she had arrived at Scutari she wrote to Sidney Herbert: 'What I have done could not have been done had I not worked with the medical authorities, and not in rivalry of them.' At the same time she had no good opinion of the medical organization of the Army, as may be judged by this extract from one of her letters—

> I do not pretend to feel any respect for the military medical profession any more than for any other race of slaves, but a strong compassion

and a burning desire to see them righted. Of me they report things which they know to be untrue, which they know that I know that they know to be untrue,—under cover of the confidential report system which is practised throughout the Army and carried to its utmost perfection by the present Inspector-General.

Of other professional organizations she was not backward in giving her opinions. When the extension of the franchise was being discussed, she wrote to Dr Sutherland—

> I won't have the College of Physicians represented, nor the Apothecaries. What! give the franchise to the greatest credulity in the world, to the blindest adherence to prejudice and predestination— to the most obstinate opposition to all fact and experience—don't give it to the physicians or I'll get up an examination and everyone of them will be plucked. You may give it to the surgeons if you like, because they are better, but only because Mr Paget has made them so.

She understood some of the professional prejudices. When she was undertaking propaganda for the removal of St Thomas's Hospital to a new site she made the following comment—

> I think it best not to try the medical papers because they will be up in arms about their Schools!—in reading any book about nursing I am always struck by the advance that common sense has made lately upon *medical* sense. If I were a mother I should dismiss a nurse for doing what Dr W. recommends as very great light, as being very great darkness.

In propagating her sanitary gospel she was usually discreet and moderate, and, rather surprisingly, she even tried to persuade her more enthusiastic friends to moderate their too strong statements. In February 1858 she wrote to Mr Chadwick concerning an article which he had been asked to write—

> Mr Herbert has told me that the Quarterly wants you after all. But I have also heard that there is some dread of your prowess in sanitary matters and of the probability of your hitting rather too hard for the heads of the usual readers of that periodical. If from past experience the people have reason to dread such a 'dressing', might it not be well to deal with them 'as if you loved them' and while stating the case and its remedies fully and openly to leave the inferences to us, the readers, as far as possible. It has occurred to me to mention this to you. Whatever view you take, I am sure you will do the wisest.

2

A remarkably clever letter to a strong-minded man whose out-spokenness often gave offence.

She had little respect for the opinions of doctors regarding the healthiness or otherwise of the situation of the hospital to which they were attached. Thus she wrote—

> It is almost impossible to get the opinions of the practising physicians and surgeons of a hospital as to its healthiness; so many interests prevent them from even investigating the circumstances which would lead to any opinion worth giving: e.g. in London one always hears that the hospital must be in the heart of a great thoroughfare 'because of the accidents.'

Early in her career she learnt that medical men have their weaknesses like other people. When she acted as superintendent of nursing at the Harley Street hospital she was under the administrative control both of a ladies' committee and of a medical committee. There were some reforms which were needed and which she wished to get introduced. To facilitate their introduction, to lessen opposition and avoid unnecessary discussion, she herself embodied the chief changes in the form of five resolutions which she dealt with in the manner recounted to her father (3 December 1853)—

> All these I proposed and carried in Committee without telling them that they came from me and not from the medical men; and then, and not till then, I showed them to the medical men, without telling them that they were already passed in Committee. It was a bold stroke but success is said to make an insurrection into a revolution. The medical men have had two meetings upon them and approved them *nem. con.* and thought they were their own. And I came off with flying colours, no one suspecting my intrigue, which of course would ruin me if it were known, as there is as much jealousy in the Committee of one another, and among the medical men of one another, as ever What's his name had of Marlborough.

Few of Miss Nightingale's contemporaries knew so much about hospitals as she did. When she was asked by the members of the Sanitary Commission in 1857 what British and foreign hospitals she had visited, she made this astonishing answer—

> I have visited all the hospitals in London, Dublin, Edinburgh, many county hospitals, some of the naval and military hospitals in England;

all the hospitals in Paris and studied with the Sœurs de Charité; the Institute of protestant deaconesses at Kaiserswerth on the Rhine where I was twice in training as a nurse; the hospitals in Berlin and many others in Germany, at Lyons, Rome, Alexandria, Constantinople, Brussels; also the war hospitals of the French and Sardinians.

She was at that time only thirty-seven years old.

With Miss Nightingale a visit to a hospital was not a formality. It was a time of concentrated observation. She was an acute observer and took great interest in the general layout of a hospital, as well as in the details of ward construction, sanitation and general administration, quite apart from the nursing side of the work. It was no wonder that she was consulted about the plans for new hospitals. Doctors everywhere recognized her as an authority, and she obtained an unrivalled acquaintance with the plans of hospitals both in this country and in Canada, Australia, and the United States of America.

Though not medically trained, Miss Nightingale picked up a lot of useful medical information which enabled her to take an intelligent interest in matters medical, and even to criticize writings on medical subjects. One example of her confident critical judgement may here be adduced. In 1856 she was made life-governor of St Mary's Hospital, Paddington, and in 1865, when a vacancy occurred on the medical staff, she was approached by one of the candidates for the post, Dr Edward Smith, F.R.S., who solicited her vote, to be given by proxy. The request was forwarded to her by Dr Farr, who also sent on a note from Dr Smith and a copy of a book on diet which he had written. Miss Nightingale did not think much of the book and expressed her views as follows—

You ask me what I think of his Diet thesis. You must please take what I say with several grains of salt. It appears to me, if it is intended to be physiological, not to be physiological; and if it is intended to be practical, not to be practical. Take it and compare it with Lyon Playfair's article on diet in Good Words for January, and Playfair strikes one at once as master of the subject—the other not. As an illustration of what I mean I send you Dr E. Smith's Indian diet. —I pointed out to him that the statement in his own pamphlet did not at all bear out the conclusions in his note. And if the second note means anything but that he wants a vote, it means that he retracts all he said in the first. He appears to me to be continually generalizing thus on insufficient ill-digested premises, and drawing unfounded principles for conclusions. Then he always ignores that, after chemistry has done her very best to compound for exactly the best diet, nature often says she will have none of it, and she will always have something else; and that it is experience only, not chemistry, which is the ultimate appeal. But for all this, Dr Edward Smith is so universally superior to those brutes who go on without observing or concluding or generalizing at all—vide 1, the wretched medical evidence at the Holborn Union Inquiry, 2, about St Thomas's removal etc, that I should always vote for Mr E. Smith's success.

William Farr's comment was: 'You have hit off Smith exactly.' In spite of Miss Nightingale's support Dr Smith was not elected. The successful candidate was Dr (afterwards Sir) William Broadbent, who in subsequent years fully justified his appointment.

Miss Nightingale held her views, whether on the training of nurses, the theory of contagion and the need for contagion, or the sanitation of hospitals, with the utmost tenacity, and she supported them with great vigour. There is very little evidence, however, that she adopted any new medical or scientific view in the last forty years of her life. An exception to this statement was her greater sympathy with women doctors in her later years; this was shown by her choosing Miss May Thorne to be her medical adviser in the latter part of her life.

At the time when her *Notes on Hospitals* was published no one was able to explain the frequency of hospital gangrene and the almost constant suppuration in wounds. Lister's classical paper which paved the way for the banishment of sepsis did not appear till 1867, and the views he promulgated were, so far as one can gather from her writings, never adopted by her. Along with Lawson Tait and others, she attributed the increased mortality in the great metropolitan hospitals, compared with hospitals in the country, to bad sanitation. To the extent that absolute cleanliness approximates to asepsis, both she and Lawson Tait were on right lines, but neither of them ever understood fully, and certainly never accepted, the full significance and the bacterial causation of septic infection.

She knew the power of the medical profession and in her public pronouncements always tried to conciliate the doctors. Moreover, she tried to make others do the same. On 16 September 1860 she wrote to Chadwick—

> But above all I am anxious (and venture to suggest that it is most important) that the medical profession should not be indisposed to you, to the sanitary movement generally and to the Social Science Association in particular. Hitherto, to do them justice, I must say I think they behaved very well, and they have contributed their fair quota to the Social Science meetings. In particular forms of treatment they can (or the public think they can) give 'posers' to lay civilians 'interfering' in medicine. I am most anxious that this opposition should not be aroused. The sick are the most credulous of human beings. They will believe anything the 'Doctor' (whether allopathic, homeopathic or hydropathic) says to them. For their sake let us be most careful to carry the 'Doctor' with us.

Doctors and the Nurse-training Project

It is quite possible that Miss Nightingale may have formed some indefinite plan for the reform of nursing before she went to the Crimea, though we have found no evidence of this. Certain it is that one of the first, if not the first person to suggest such a plan to her was a doctor—Dr Bence Jones. Dr Bence Jones became acquainted with Miss Nightingale during the time when she was superintendent at the hospital in Harley Street. He had a high opinion of her ability, and she on her part regarded him as the best 'chemical doctor' in London. During her convalescence in the Crimea in the summer of 1855 Dr Bence Jones wrote to her saying how glad he was that she had got well from her illness, and at the same time took the opportunity to ask her advice about a project he had in mind for training nurses in London hospitals. The part of his letter which dealt with this ran as follows (10 August 1855)—

> It has become most manifest that we have at present no means for training nurses in the London hospitals. The permission that is now given to some persons is toleration, and that not very easily borne in some of our hospitals. We want something much better than this.

I have put my first thoughts on paper and send them for your corrections and improvements.

Desiderata regarding the training of nurses in London hospitals.

1. To obtain the recognition of the principle by the Governors to make it one of the objects to be attained by the Hospital on account of the benefit it may be to the sick poor and rich to have nurses well trained and their characters well known. This object being scarcely inferior to the education of medical men and almost equal to the care of the sick poor.

2. To appoint a superintendent day nurse who shall have no ward to take care of, but shall, like the present superintendent night nurse at St George's, be superior to the other nurses and shall specially direct and instruct the persons who are being trained, giving a weekly statement to the Board regarding their progress and character, and she shall ultimately certify to the Board those who are fit to be engaged by the hospital as nurses, or by private individuals.

3. To admit no persons to be trained who are not boarded or lodged either in some suitable institution or in the hospital, or who will not engage to come to the hospital as early as they may be wanted in the morning; to remain if required at the hospital for six months from the time when they began their attendance, or to cease to attend on the receipt of a written order from the superintendent nurse or from the board.

I want our Governors at St George's to adopt this but I must first persuade the medical men, and they are more difficult than the Governors I fear. However, when I return I mean to try what can be done, and if you will write me a strong letter about it giving me your own views I might find it of great use. Whatever you think of the next part of my letter pray give me more potent help in this. I care about it far more than what I am going to say, and if it costs trouble to give me the information I want, pray let it alone till we meet, if ever, in this or another world.

Before giving the second part of the letter we must point out that it is clear that Bence Jones had the firm intention of starting a nurse-training school at St George's and that he thought such schools should be general in the London hospitals. It is also clear that he anticipated the appointment of a nurse who should do nothing but teach and supervise the training of the student-nurse. When, soon after this, the national fund was raised in honour of Miss Nightingale, it was not surprising that her thoughts were influenced in the direction of founding a nurse-training school. Until I came across this letter I had been rather puzzled to find that Dr Bence Jones should have been nominated as one of the original members of the Council of the Nightingale Fund, but this letter supplies a sufficient reason.

To understand the second part of Bence Jones' letter one must explain that Miss Nightingale had been annoyed because, without previous consultation with her, a second party of nurses had been sent out to the seat of war under the charge of Miss Stanley. She had written an indignant letter of complaint to Sidney Herbert. It was not till several months later that she was given official control of all the nurses at the seat of war. Dr Bence Jones must have heard of her protests, for he writes—

> What has led you to write so strongly against more nurses coming out? How is it that your opinion of the nurses is so much worse than that of others? How is it that you seem to think the evil much outweighs the good, whilst others think the good outweighs the evil. What is the evil and the exact amount? Is the principle of the whole thing a failure to drop entirely when you cease to move it? Why is it a failure? I have heard such different accounts and I have found the Governments so changeable in their intention regarding nurses going that I should like to know the exact state of the case. That you would do your work and overdo it no one knew better than I did, but I doubted the general working and I should like to hear the particulars which have led to the discouragement of the undertaking, to your not carrying it out to the extent it should be carried if it was altogether good. I fear you will say that this is too long a story for your time and many engagements.

It would have been interesting to read Miss Nightingale's reply, but it is not to be found among her papers.

As related in a later chapter Miss Nightingale was not in favour of teaching nurses too much pure medicine, for she thought it would make them either intolerable from airing their knowledge, or miserable, presumably from seeing methods adopted which were not in keeping with the methods which they had been taught were the best. In March 1873 she wrote to Mr Croft: 'The one extreme danger in these days is that nurses shall fancy themselves "medical women".' In forming this opinion she may have been looking into her own heart and judging from her own experience. In her work in the Harley Street hospital, and still more in her vast Crimean experience, she had picked up a lot of practical medicine, and this had led her to be ready to express her views on medical matters and to criticize freely the views and treatment advised by various doctors. There is little doubt that, given suitable training, she would have made an excellent physician. She understood the correct psychological approach to patients. In a letter written to Lady Herbert on 10 April 1861 she commented—

> Medicine is a mere matter of experience of which we do not yet know the rules. If I were a doctor I never would argue with my patient, because then 'he' thinks his argument may be as good as mine. I would say 'this' is the matter, 'that' is what you are to do. If you don't do it, send me away.

That puts the correct medical attitude in a nutshell.

However, with commendable restraint Miss Nightingale sometimes suppressed her opinion, as related in a letter to Sir J. McNeill (16 October 1860)—

> the littlest Clough, who with his sister is here, has got a thing which I call tooth-rash but which the doctor calls measles. (Perhaps this is a new sort of measles since my time.) However I always support mothers and doctors against myself, and therefore, although the child is hurra-ing at this moment I think it right to tell you.

But she sometimes served as a good illustration of her own argument that too much knowledge of medicine in a nurse may have uncalled-for results. When Sidney Herbert was very ill with disease of the kidneys, she did not hesitate to give him a great deal of dogmatic advice both as to whom he should consult and what treatment he ought to adopt. She wrote to Lady Herbert (on 10 April 1861) concerning her husband's illness—

> If he would observe five things he might consult Tom [the kitten] and it would do just as well as 'Ben Jonson' [Bence Jones] or French. These are (some of them he does already, I know)
>
> 1. Eating as much good food as he can (not sauces or acid such as acid fruits) and drinking claret. French tells him to eat beef and beer because 'that makes blood'. So did Sganarelli tell the

dumb woman to take wine and bread because that made parrots talk. 'Vite, vite, quantité de pain et de vin.'

2. Clothing warmly and wearing a flannel belt round the body. This Grainger, who has albuminaria of a very advanced stage and fancies he has granular disease of the kidneys, which he has not, lays great stress upon.

3. Doing no night-society which he can possibly help. One night-party is worth ten days illness to him.

4. Sleep out of doors, that is out of London.

5. Taking his exercise regularly in the fresh air especially in the fresh morning air. If he would do these things he might never see Ben Jonson again.

But she went even farther than this. She was confident that she could judge the merits of prescriptions, though she had little confidence in any of them. Thus she writes—

But for God's sake never adopt any treatment which tends to lower the powers of life. If I could see your prescriptions I could at all events tell you this.

She was certainly correct in asserting that there was no curative treatment for renal disease then known to the physicians, but her dogmatism as to the nature of the disease from which Lord Herbert was at that time suffering was, to say the least, surprising (31 May 1861)—

There is no great use in physic either way. You can't help nature much in that way. There is no proof that he has organic disease—other than incipient. There is proof that he has blood disease i.e. that he is in a state of thorough London ill-health with poverty of blood which deposits albumen, which physic will neither materially add to nor take away. That organic disease may at any time be set up (whether morbus Brightii or not B. J. himself does not know) and his capital error was in arguing from the presence of albumen that there was organic kidney disease.

Your capital error is, if I may say so, in thinking that four days will cure him, or that four days will kill him, and in being correspondingly elated or despondent.

She was insistent to see the prescriptions—

If you mean to go on with French would you let me see his prescriptions. At least I could give you an opinion upon them. You need not take it.

She held the fallacious view that it was possible to understand a person's constitution by constant association with them, for in one letter she wrote—

> there are two men about whose constitutions (and only two) I think I can speak with confidence. Because it is impossible for an old nurse like me to see a man every day without learning him off by heart (one is 'he' and the other Mr Clough).

The 'he' referred to Lord Herbert. It is a melancholy fact that both the men to whom she referred so confidently died within eight months of her writing this letter.

2

The Doctor who slaved for Miss Nightingale

DR JOHN SUTHERLAND (1808–1891)

FLORENCE NIGHTINGALE possessed an amazing power of enlisting the devoted help of men of great ability in many walks of life. They admired her high intelligence, they recognized her selfless devotion to a noble cause, and, after she had become a semi-invalid, they pitied her weakness, while wondering at the vitality which sustained her in her debilitated condition. On her part Miss Nightingale was usually deferential in her approach to those whose assistance she hoped to gain, but when she had gained their support, she speedily pressed home her advantage, endeavoured to make them enthusiastic in the cause, and demanded, and usually succeeded in obtaining, their whole-hearted endeavour. Some of them so far identified themselves with her aims that they were like brothers to her—brothers whom she could order about, scold, tease, and occasionally, very occasionally, praise—much as exacting sisters treat tolerant and docile brothers. She fully recognized her own remarkable powers, and once in a letter to Madame Mohl (13 December 1861) she boasted of her ability to change certain men's lives. Madame Mohl expressed the opinion that women were more sympathetic than men. Miss Nightingale replied that if she were to write a book out of her own experience she would begin with the words 'Women have no sympathy.' She continued—

I have never found one woman who has altered her life by one iota for me or my opinions. Now look at my experience of men. A statesman, past middle age, absorbed in politics for a quarter of a century, out of sympathy with me remodels his whole life and policy, learns a science the driest, the most technical, the most difficult, that of administration, as far as it concerns the life of man—not as I learnt it in the field from stirring experience, but by writing dry regulations by my sofa with me. This is what I call real sympathy. Another, Alexander (whom I made Director-General), does very nearly the same thing. He is dead, too. Clough, a poet born if ever there was one, takes to nursing administration in the same way, for me. But I could mention very many others—Farr, McNeill, Tulloch, Storks, Martin, who in a lesser degree have altered their work by my opinions. And, most wonderful of all, a man born without a soul like Undine—all these elderly men.

Of the nine men mentioned in this list five were doctors, and the one whom she thus designated as a man born without a soul— Dr John Sutherland—was the man who for more than thirty years helped and sustained her more than anyone else, and identified himself with her life-work as closely as it was possible for anyone to do. The relationship between Florence Nightingale and Dr Sutherland was such as seldom exists in real life and merits fuller description.

Dr Sutherland was born in Edinburgh in 1808. He studied medicine at Edinburgh University, qualified at the Edinburgh College of Surgeons in 1827, and took an M.D. in 1831. For a time he travelled on the Continent, then came back and began medical practice in Liverpool, where he took an active interest in matters of public health. He became associated with Dr W. H. Duncan, who in 1847 was appointed the first medical officer of health in this country. For a time Sutherland edited the Liverpool *Health of Towns Advocate*. In 1848 he became an inspector under the first Board of Health. He attended the Paris Conference on Quarantine and was decorated by Louis Napoleon. He investigated the matter of intra-mural burial and in relation to that subject was granted an interview with the Pope. In 1855 when there was a great outcry about the sanitary conditions of our army in the East, Sutherland was sent out as the chief medical member of the Commission appointed to inquire into the sanitary conditions at the seat of war. He was then forty-seven years of age. He arrived at Scutari on 6 March 1855. He there became acquainted with Miss

Nightingale, with whom he must have discussed the sanitary problems which he was investigating. Miss Nightingale admitted that it was from Dr Sutherland that she gained all the sanitary knowledge she possessed, and, though that may have been an exaggeration, it is certain that he was the main source of her wide knowledge of sanitary science.

When Dr Sutherland went on from Scutari to the Crimea he still remained her counsellor. Miss Nightingale's instructions from the War Office had been to superintend the nurses in Turkey. No mention had been made of Russia, in which the Crimea was situated. In view of the opposition she encountered from official quarters she was doubtful whether she would be justified in visiting the Crimea, and in her dilemma she wrote to Dr Sutherland asking his advice. He suggested that she should write home and ask the War Department to place her authority on a proper footing before she went to Balaklava. Her visit of inspection was approved by the War Office, and in April 1855 she was given the appointment of Almoner of the Free Gifts in all the British Hospitals in the Crimea. This was not exactly what she wanted, and it was not till ten months later that she was given officially the full control of the British nurses in the Crimea.

The meeting of Miss Nightingale and Dr Sutherland at Scutari was the beginning of a thirty-six year period during which he acted as her trusty and trusted confidential adviser. Mrs Woodham-Smith puts the case in a brilliant sentence: 'He met Miss Nightingale at Scutari, became her slave, and his career was at an end.' There is truth in this, but not the whole truth. Sir Edward Cook is more matter-of-fact in his description: 'In Dr Sutherland the head of the Sanitary Commission, Miss Nightingale found a warm admirer and a stout supporter. During his stay at Scutari he acted as her physician, on her return to England she was on terms of intimate friendship with him and his wife; and Dr Sutherland was, as we shall hear, one of her close allies in the battle for reform in Army Hygiene.' This description is also true, but it is very much less than the whole truth.

It is hardly correct to say that Dr Sutherland's association with

Miss Nightingale put an end to his career. On the contrary, their collaboration enabled Dr Sutherland's abilities to be used in a wider field, and permitted him to exert a greater influence both at home and abroad than he otherwise would have been likely to do. As Inspector of the Board of Health he had reached almost as far as he could go, unless he had entered the political arena, for which he had neither liking nor aptitude. By joining Miss Nightingale in the great scheme of Army sanitary reform both at home and in India he found a very fruitful occupation which absorbed his energies until he was over eighty years of age—at least fifteen more years than his former career would have allowed him. From 1856 to 1872 Miss Nightingale occupied an extraordinarily interesting and influential position. Though she had no official position, she had in effect the power of a Cabinet Minister without portfolio, dealing with various aspects of Army reform. Cabinet Ministers and Viceroys of India sought her opinion and followed her advice. She virtually had in her power the nominations to the Sub-Commissions which carried out the recommendations of the main Army Sanitary Commission of 1856–8.

Dr Sutherland was by Miss Nightingale's influence nominated one of the members of the main Commission in 1856, and in the next year he was appointed to the membership of the Barracks and Hospitals Sub-Commission; he remained on this and on the Army Sanitary Committee (to which its name was changed in 1863) until 1888. From 1859 to 1863 he served as a member of the Royal Commission on India. In addition to these commitments he served on several other commissions or committees which dealt with the barracks and hospitals in the Mediterranean, and with the provision of institutes and day-rooms for the soldiers. He did much more than this. He acted as confidential secretary to Miss Nightingale. He was her constant adviser in the many problems which were presented to her from all over the world on a great variety of subjects, particularly on the construction of hospitals, the training of nurses, the organization of poor-law infirmaries, and many sanitary problems. Moreover, though Miss Nightingale often treated him rather cavalierly, he had the satisfaction that she

usually took his advice. For a man who was not personally am-
bitious, this must have been a satisfying career. Even financially
he cannot have been a loser. He was a paid member of the Sanitary
Committee, maintained his position long after the usual retiring
age in the Civil Service, and left a much larger fortune than did
Miss Nightingale.

His position on the Army Sanitary Committee was unique.
Miss Nightingale had insisted (and gained her point) that the
Hospital Sub-Commission, and later the Sanitary Committee,
should not be under the authority of the Army Medical Department, but should report and be responsible directly to the Secretary of State. This meant in effect that Miss Nightingale and Dr
Sutherland had an entirely free hand. She could even joke about it.
Writing to Dr Farr on 13 October 1866 she informed him that
'Dr Sutherland returns home today from Gibralter. I understand
it is said—"he must report to Miss Nightingale or to himself, for
there is no one else to report to at the War Office". Don't repeat
this bad joke.'

Dr Sutherland was a man of sound common sense. He had a
practical experience of matters relating to public health and was
an expert in sanitation. He had not the burning enthusiasm nor
the vivid imagination of his colleague, but he knew the best way
to get things done and realized the limits of what was possible
under any particular circumstances. Miss Nightingale was fuller
of ideas and quicker of perception than Dr Sutherland; she had
much greater drive and will-power, but she did not possess his
equanimity. Between them, working together, much greater
achievements were accomplished than would ever have been done
by either of them working alone. In one letter to Dr Sutherland
she enunciated a principle which was very far ahead of her time—

> What we say is that a State, if it is to be a State at all, must supply for
> its willing workers in the State or out of it the means to work so as
> to learn a livelihood—and to its criminals the means to work their
> way out of prison.

At the beginning of their partnership Dr Sutherland not only
admired but almost had some affection towards Miss Nightingale,

and to the end of his life he remained her faithful friend. She on her side always acknowledged the great debt she owed to Dr Sutherland but her imaginative spirit soared above his practical genius and she frequently betrayed impatience of his more humdrum but certainly more serviceable suggestions. Two short extracts from letters will show how her domineering spirit overruled him. In a letter to Dr McNeill (27 June 1857) she wrote—

> Sutherland does not carry the weight in the Commission which his brains ought to give him and he lets very inferior men put him down owing to his want of pith. It vexes me and upsets the conclusions I want to impress upon Mr Herbert.

Again, in a letter to Dr Farr dated 28 September 1861 she wrote—

> Dr Sutherland will not be back and he must be examined again. I told him his evidence was very tame and he thought so too. There is a great deal more to be said.

The close collaboration between the two is attested by the very numerous communications which passed between them during the thirty years they worked together. Though Miss Nightingale was the virtual director of their conjoint work, she insisted on remaining in the background.

To give the reader some idea of the depth and detail of Dr Sutherland's knowledge of the aims Miss Nightingale had in view, and the wise counsel he was able to give her, we will transcribe the letter he sent her on 25 August 1856, immediately after her return from the Crimea and just before she went to see Queen Victoria at Balmoral. It is a good example of countless similar letters he sent her.

> My dear Miss Nightingale,
>
> I have just received your letter of the 24th, and am very glad to find you are so well as to write so long a letter containing so many questions. Depend on the whole matter being kept by me in strict confidence, and I now proceed to give you (the) best advice I can.
>
> 1. It appears to me that your own good sense has pointed out the reply which should be given to Sir B. H. [Benjamin Hawes]. You are in a position to give advice which ought *not* to be rejected. It would be extremely difficult to enter into all the details of the nursing management of hospitals so as to make them clear to persons not only

1. Dr Henry Bence Jones (1814–73)

(Drawn by George Richmond, engraved by Charles Hill. Engraving in possession of the Royal Society of Medicine)

2. Dr John Sutherland (1808–91), who was the confidential adviser of Miss
Nightingale for over thirty years

(From 'The Illustrated London News', 1891)

unaccustomed to such management, but prejudiced against it, and even if they were made thoroughly to comprehend it and had every wish to carry it out, the greatest of all difficulties would still remain, namely, the art of doing so. You know full well that nursing is not a paper science, but a very difficult art, and from these considerations my opinion is that there is no hope for the improvement we all desire to see carried out, except in introducing them gradually and steadily until they become incorporated with an improved hospital service.

2. I see no reason, since you have determined not to send the suggestions asked for, why you might not offer to introduce into the home military hospitals an element which has never hitherto existed in them—that of female nursing! to an extent which you *define*, but I would recommend you not to call it *reform*.

3. I entirely agree with you as to taking no action at the present time in the matter of the Nightingale Fund. John Bull's organ of wonder is too much excited to enable him to arrive at any practical conclusions on the subject. It is being discussed, however, and from what I myself have heard I have every hope of its assuming a real working form.

4. I think you should tell Lord Panmure fully and openly your experiences in the East. He has every desire to carry out such improvements as would benefit the public service. What he really wants is good reliable information. When you see Her Majesty your conversation with Her Majesty may take a form you might not be prepared for. You will have to be guided by circumstances both as to the information you may communicate and any request you may make. I would recommend you not to go prepared with any definite request as to having a female nursing establishment, but of course as I have already said, you will be guided by the turn the conversation may take. I should not think it probable that you will have an opportunity of entering into the question of Army medical reform with the Queen. There is no reason, however, why you should not do so with Lord Panmure. In that case I would advise you to restrict your conversation to the defects which have come under your notice, and not to suggest any reform unless asked to do so. Facts are always facts, while advice may be returned without thanks, which in your case it is better to avoid. Unfortunately there are great differences of opinion as to what is required to reform the Army Medical Department. The scientific defects could be easily remedied, but those defects you point at are not I fear of such easy removal. They are the fruit of the Army system generally, and until the tree is rendered good such

3

will be the produce. One comfort is that in all the European armies the medical system has been improving and had improved immeasurably within a century. The late war has raised the British Army greatly, at least in matters of detail, and I for one have every hope that your own work, like every true and good thing, will leave its impress on the great highway of human progress.

I hope you will enjoy your visit to Balmoral. It is a beautiful spot. You will also no doubt go to Birkdale where I am sure you will meet with a warm reception. I dined with Sir James the other day and we talked over 'your case' but I fear from the character of your letter that you have already escaped our hands.

I am yours ever faithfully

JOHN SUTHERLAND.

This letter is full of common sense and wise advice. Dr Sutherland had himself had an interview with Queen Victoria on his return from the Crimea and was therefore in a position to give useful advice as to Miss Nightingale's prospective interview.

The correspondence which continued for thirty years varied from time to time in tone: usually business-like, occasionally playful, sometimes anxious, and rarely almost affectionate. It is interesting to note the gradual change in their relationship. Early in the correspondence Dr Sutherland realized the greatness of Miss Nightingale's aims, which were beyond anything he had imagined, and the power of her will, which was soon made manifest to him. In a letter he wrote on 12 November 1856 he said—

> I have just received your letter of yesterday and am led to believe that there must be a foundation of truth under the old myth about the Amazon women somewhere to the east of Scutari. All I can say is that if you had been queen of that respectable body in old days, Alexander the Great would have had rather a bad chance. Your project has developed itself far better than I expected and therefore I shall serve on the Commission.

The reference to the Amazons appears to have been taken in good part. A few years later, however, an attempt at levity was not so well received. On 13 January 1859 Sutherland finished a letter as follows—

> It is not often I can find a legitimate ground of quarrel with you, and I am always glad when I can do so. Your note of this morning

arrived *open* and all the grave secrets exposed to the gaze of the post-man—'Think of that, Mr Shallow.'

This time he must have given serious offence, for judging by the letter he received dated 15 January he must have got a rap on the knuckles. In the next letter he humbly apologizes—

> I hope my remarks about your note being open did not pain you. I only said it in fun. What I wrote to your mother was simply an expression of my intense anxiety about you, so pray forgive me.

There is no doubt that in the early years he worried greatly about her health. He was constantly asking how she felt and frequently advised her to take a complete rest. Her heart and her very life were in her work and she neither would nor could rest. She got to that debilitated and nervous condition when every suggestion of taking a rest irritated her beyond measure. In September 1857 Sutherland was voicing his own genuine anxiety as well as that of her family when he wrote to her while she was taking an enforced rest at Malvern.

> Pray leave us all to ourselves, soldiers and all, for a while. We shall all be better for a rest. Even your divine Pan will be more musical for not being beaten quite so much. As for Mr Sidney Herbert he must be in the seventh heaven. Please do not gull Dr Gully but do eat and drink, and don't think. We'll make such a precious row when you come back. The day you left town it appeared as if all your blood wanted renewing, and that cannot be done in a week. You must have new blood or you can't work, and new blood can't be made out of tea, at least as far as I know.—And now I have done my duty as a confessor, and hope I shall find you an obedient penitent.

Not a bit of it. This letter produced a very long reply (5 September 1857) which showed that even if she were physically weak, Miss Nightingale was mentally very alert.

> And what shall I say in answer to your letter? Someone once said 'He that would save his life shall lose it; and what should it profit a man if he gain the whole world and lose his own soul?' He meant, I suppose, that 'life' is a means and not an end. Perhaps he was right. Now in what respect could I have done other than I have done? Or what exertion have I made that I could have left unmade?—Had I

'lost' the Report, what would the health I should have saved 'profited' me? Or what would ten years of life have advantaged me, exchanged for ten weeks this summer?

Yes, but you say, you might have walked or driven, or eaten meat. Well, since we must come to *sentir della spezieria*, let me tell you, O doctor, that after any walk or drive I sat up all night with palpitations, and the sight of animal food increased the sickness. The man here put me, as soon as I arrived, on a sofa and told me not to move, and to take no solid food at all, till my pulse came down. I remind myself of a little dog, a friend of mine, who barked himself out of an apoplectic fit when the dog-doctor did something he had always manifested an objection to. Now I have written myself into a palpitation.

She then went on to liken the critical advice which had been offered her by so many friends to the vision she had had of a canary pecking at the body of her dead pet owl, and finished by asserting that she is not a penitent, even though he may claim to be a confessor. The whole of the letter was obviously the product of an overwrought mind. The reply of Dr Sutherland to this tirade was a model of good sense, and showed, perhaps better than anything else he wrote, how wide of the truth was the accusation that he had 'no soul' (7 September 1857)—

What can I say, my dear friend, to your long scold of a letter? You are decidedly wrong in passing yourself off as a dead owl, and in thinking that I have joined with other equally charitable people in pecking at you. It is I that have got all the pecking, although I hope that I am neither an owl or dead; and your little beak is one of the sharpest. But like a good live hero I bear it joyfully because it is got in doing my duty to you. I want you to live. I want you to work. You want to work and die, and that is not at all fair. I admire your heroism and self-devotion with all my heart, but alas! I cannot forget that it is all within the compass of a weak perishing body; and am I to encourage you to wear yourself in the vain attempt to beat, not only men, but time? You little know what daily anxiety it has cost me to see you dying by inches in doing work fit only for the strongest constitutions. One thing is quite clear, that women can do what men would not do, and that women will dare suffering knowingly where men would shrink. If they (the Commissions) were issued you would have some rest, and I would have work, which is the only thing I care for. Sanitary 'talk' and sanitary 'writing' are worse than useless while people are dying, and it is so much easier to work.

Miss Nightingale was a hard taskmistress both to herself and to her assistants, and at times she was an unjust critic. On 8 February 1859 Sutherland complained: 'Your letter this morning has made me very very sorry,' and the next day he openly lamented: 'Why did you send me such a note? If you only knew the pain you have given me. Every word you write I take *au sérieux*. I believe everything of you but you believe nothing of me. You have the entire advantage and you must ever have it, whatever you say.'

Occasionally, owing to pressure of work at his office, Sutherland found it difficult to make headway with work he was doing for Miss Nightingale. He got no sympathy from his censorious colleague. In 1870 she wrote him: 'I am too ill to move, probably. But I shall not put off my departure day after day indefinitely—risking my life where others will not risk a few hours labour.' Sutherland replied mildly: 'It is not a few hours labour. It is doing compulsory work. But there is no reason for putting it off. I mean office work.'

Even when he was ill he got little sympathy. It was in the same year (1870) that he received the following note: 'I am sorry you are ill. But I suppose as I have not heard again that you intend me to believe that you are either well or dead. I am so busy that I have no time to die.'

Some idea of the frequency of the correspondence between them may be obtained by noting the number of letters which passed between them in January and February 1859. There are letters still available from Dr Sutherland to Miss Nightingale dated 13, 15, 18, 22 January and 3, 7, 8, 9, 10 and 12 February, and we must assume from the nature of the contents that on the intervening dates letters were despatched from Miss Nightingale to Dr Sutherland in equal numbers. In addition he constantly attended at her residence to advise her on daily problems. Sometimes she discussed matters in a personal interview, but he was rather deaf and this annoyed her. Sometimes they communicated in writing even when in each other's presence. On a scrap of paper still preserved can be seen the following complaint from Miss Nightingale—

> Now *are* you going to sit there? I was so ill on Thursday and Tuesday from leaning forward to shout at you. You make me write reams about what Sir B[artle F[rere] tells me, and you won't tell me a word.

On another occasion she wrote down—

> Yes, and when I do show you anything, you say 'I saw that.' You had commented to me that information 15 times this morning. Why, man, do you think, man, that I shew you things to hear that?

Sometimes he was not allowed an interview but they communicated by writing from one room to the other. On one occasion a scrap of paper was used which had some writing on it which ends: 'Has the man gone?', indicating probably that 'the man's' patience had become exhausted. A perusal of the correspondence shows that the doctor advised Miss Nightingale on almost every project which she took in hand. She once asked Sutherland to solve a domestic medical problem: 'Could you tell me what the enclosed pills are? . . . Would you believe it that the maids of the mistress, of the supposed greatest authority on nursing take quack remedies.' Dr Sutherland advised her to send the maid to a doctor, and added, 'the nearer to Rome the less the religion.'

She had an amazing power of grasping detail, of accumulating statistics, of estimating motives and of judging character, but it was Sutherland who seized the essentials of a problem, who saw more clearly the proportions of things and who brought her theoretical conclusions to the touchstone of reality. Gradually she came to depend on him to sift the wheat from the chaff in the numerous communications and memoranda she received. He was reliable and trustworthy and she had complete confidence in his judgement. In December 1871 she wrote him—

> I am asked to write in a newspaper article the essence of several volumes. . . . If you chose to put down a series of little axioms for me to enlarge upon and write in my own style (as I did in the India letters) that would be a different thing—and I would undertake it.

She became so dependent upon him that when he was away she was quite at a loss. On 19 January 1866 she wrote to Dr Farr—

> Dr Sutherland has been sent to Algeria—and I have all his business besides my own to do.—It is just like two men going into business with a million each. The one suddenly withdraws. The other may wear himself to the bone, but he can't meet the engagements with one million which he made with two.—Bless your heart, Dr Sutherland thinks the world moves round himself, and that all business stops naturally till he comes back.

Miss Nightingale had a remarkable gift of expression and a logical power which enabled her to clothe Dr Sutherland's plain sensible prose in a garment of eloquent language. Her great reputation ensured that whatever she wrote would gain attention, but it ought to be remembered that many of her arguments and much of her policy were guided by the matter-of-fact doctor whose close contact with reality was interpreted as 'lack of soul' by his more imaginative colleague. He even gave her most useful advice as to how she should proceed to write the famous *Notes on Nursing*. Before she began to write he gave her this piece of advice—

> If you come to teach nursing to the class of people from whom nurses are taken you will have to be simpler and write in precept, illustrating the precepts by a few easy sentences requiring little thought but appealing to an element that every good nurse must have, namely, common sense. This strikes me as the general plan of such a manual.

When he saw the manual in rough manuscript he went further—

> I would soften down the doctrines on the first page because they would be disputed by some men of name, and the general tenor of the criticism would, I fear, set the M.D.'s against you and stave off improvement. It is very important not to offend the doctors. If I were you I should go on with it. Get out all your ideas on the subject of nursing and all your experiences. Never mind the arrangement. The great thing is to get the ideas into tangible shape. There are many in these papers very valuable and which indicate others. I should feel disposed also to go more into detail as to distinction between the different clans of nursing, for instance, hospital nurses, domestic nursing by paid nurses, and domestic nursing by mothers, sisters etc, and I would put in a petition for a few words on that kind of nursing which most nearly touches my feelings, namely, nursing the

poor in their own homes, and how charitable women could go about quietly and unostentatiously and without letting their left hand know what is done by their right hand. You might draw such a picture as would draw all hearts to it.

He concluded the letter with a practical suggestion—

This strikes me as the general plan of such a manual most certain to forward the work. Why should you not make it a legacy to the Fund? At all events go on, put together all your thoughts in any order they come to you, and you can easily cut out and arrange afterwards. It will be the least fatiguing process in your present state of health. As we intend to get 'common things' introduced into the schools, don't forget that also. God bless you and give you strength for such a work.

In the course of their common campaign they met much opposition from officialdom. In February 1859 Sutherland commented upon this—

All this is very hopeful and must tell on the dolts we have to deal with, if ever anything tells on dolts, which is doubtful. A dolt is a person who, without any merit or competency gets into a public appointment and spends his life and draws his salary in keeping himself in office and keeping out all improvement. This is a new definition which may perhaps be useful some day or other.

The best testimony of the high regard in which Miss Nightingale held Dr Sutherland is that, at a time when she thought she had not long to live, she made her will in which she directed that he should be asked to look after her private papers. This was in February 1862.

Dr Sutherland to collect and take into his possession all the official books, MSS, Returns, Indian replies, etc, which I have, belonging to Government Commissions and offices. Also to select for himself my Blue Books or other books (referring to these Commissions and their business) of mine. Also the papers referring to Colonial schools and hospitals, and those referring to the statistical returns of Associations to go to him—with an earnest request that he and Dr Farr will make such use of them as may seem to them best. Also I earnestly request Dr Sutherland to edit the edition of my Notes on Hospitals, as promised for me by Mr Clough a year ago to Messrs Parker, omitting all that relates to the Crimean War, adding whatever seems to him desirable, but not altering anything which regards nurses, ward offices or the nursing administration generally; and I beg that Dr Sutherland will accept due pecuniary compensation for such editing.

She made a similar request in 1869 when once more she thought that she had not long to live.

Dr Sutherland never, so far as we can find, accepted the 'germ' theory of disease, and similarly Miss Nightingale opposed that view energetically and all her working life, and this in spite of the fact that some of her close friends such as Farr and Parkes felt compelled to admit as true at least a part of the new doctrine.

The remarkable partnership lasted till 1888, when Sutherland, at the age of eighty years, felt compelled to retire. He did not long survive his retirement for he died in 1891 (July 14th). His end is thus described by Sir Edward Cook—

He was in great weakness at the end, and was hardly able to read or to speak; but his wife said she had received a letter from Miss Nightingale with messages for him. To her surprise he roused himself once more, read the letter through, and said 'Give her my love and blessing.' They were almost his last words.

3

The Doctors in the Crimea

WHEN MISS NIGHTINGALE arrived at Scutari the attitude of the medical officers of the Army towards her was at first indifferent, if not antagonistic. Some few appeared to resent her coming and threw difficulties in her path. This was not altogether surprising. Women had never previously nursed on active service abroad, and it was doubtful how they would accommodate themselves to the unusual circumstances. None of the medical officers would or could know that Miss Nightingale possessed outstanding administrative abilities, nor was anyone aware that she was endued with a remarkable capacity for intensive and prolonged activity and responsibility. She herself perfectly understood the nature and necessity of discipline, and she conformed scrupulously to regulations. She refused to enter any ward, or to allow any of her subordinates to enter any ward, except at the request of the medical officer in charge of that ward. It was not long, however, before the overwhelming number of sick and wounded compelled all the medical officers to ask for her help, and, once her assistance had been given, it was appreciated and welcomed. Ten days after her arrival at Scutari she wrote to Dr (afterwards Sir) William Bowman as follows—

We are very lucky in our medical heads. Two of them are brutes and four are angels—for this is a work which makes either angels or devils of men, and of women too. As for the assistants, they are all cubs, and will, while a man is breathing his last breath under the knife, lament the 'annoyance of being called up from their dinners by such a fresh influx of wounded.' But unlicked cubs grow up into good old bears, though I don't know how; for certain it is, the old bears are good.

By skill in nursing, and still more by efficient administration, she soon gained an established position. As she wrote on 15 December 1854: 'I have toiled my way into the confidence of the medical men.'

From the purely nursing point of view her position was never again seriously challenged by the doctors. She was, however, much more than a superintendent of nursing. She was a woman of vision, the first woman of commanding intellect who had ever been privileged to see how sick and wounded soldiers were cared for at the front under conditions of active service. What she saw was so indelibly engraven on her mind that most of the rest of her long life was devoted to trying to remedy the deficiencies of the Army medical and nursing services. At the time she did her best by all means in her power to improve the conditions in the hospitals, and almost inevitably she provoked the latent and occasionally the active opposition of the principal medical officer, Dr (afterwards Sir) John Hall, and some of his subordinates.

Three weeks after her arrival in the East she wrote a private letter to Sidney Herbert, the Minister of War, in which she recorded the lamentable state of affairs, and her remarks show that she had a clear idea as to the cause of the trouble.

> The fault here is not with the medical officers, but in the separation of the department which affords every necessary supply except medicine to them, and in the insufficiency of minor officers in the purveying department.

She found that she could not obtain articles necessary for the patients from the purveyor without a long delay, and sometimes they were refused though known to be in stock. Fortunately she had at her disposal some private funds, and she obtained great help from Mr Macdonald, who administered *The Times* Fund. By this means she was able to buy many necessaries in the open market at Constantinople. She failed to see why the purveyor, the commissary officers and the principal medical officer did not avail themselves of this source of supply. She thought it ridiculous that the army system could not adapt itself so as to obtain urgent requirements. Starting without any personal antagonisms, she was yet no respecter of persons, lay or medical, when she met with wilful opposition.

An early reform which she initiated was one calculated to help the medical officers in their work, namely, the institution of a proper system of orderlies in the wards. Under the old system men were taken from the ranks to help in the wards, often men who were 'quite ignorant of everything connected with a hospital.' They were, moreover, liable to be recalled to their regiment at any moment, so that there was no guarantee of continuity of service by experienced men in the wards. It was owing to Miss Nightingale's representations to Mr Herbert in September 1855 that a Royal Warrant was issued for the reorganization of the Medical Staff Corps. This Warrant provided trained ward-orderlies specially chosen for their task.

On the general question of sanitation she was well ahead of her time, and she was shocked by the insanitary conditions of the wards at the Barrack Hospital in which she was working. At first it surprised her that the medical officers did not complain or make any effort to remedy the conditions which were so obviously unhealthy. It did not take her long to find out one reason for this. On 8 January 1855 she wrote to Mr Herbert—

> You will never hear the whole truth, troublesome as it is, except from one independent of promotion. . . . The medical officers if they were to betray them, would have it 'reported personally and professionally to their disadvantage.' I have no compassion for the men who would rather see hundreds of lives lost than waive one scruple of the official conscience.

Her view was that many medical officers would do their best to obtain much-needed reforms but for their fear of getting a bad report from their seniors. She found a few who were sympathetic with her views, and, to the best of their ability, co-operated with her projects for improvement. Dr McGrigor was one of those who helped her considerably in her individual effort to prepare an extra wing of the hospital for reception of patients. She wrote privately to Sidney Herbert asking him to promote McGrigor to the rank of Deputy Inspector-General, and this was done. Then

McGrigor fell from grace because he did not consult her so often
and appeared to be coming under the influence of an officer who
had not so much sympathy with her.

When the inquiry instigated by Mr Stafford was being conducted Miss Nightingale wrote home to say that there were a
number of medical officers who, if they were called before the
Committee, would give reliable evidence. In addition to Major-
General Alexander, she gave the names of three staff-surgeons
first class, and two regimental surgeons, who could be relied on to
give a true account of the state of affairs. She added that she had
no doubt there were many others who would do the same. About
the attitude of some medical officers she was rather bitter.

> Of me they report things which they know to be untrue, which they
> know that I know that they know to be untrue—under cover of the
> confidential report system which is practised throughout the Army
> and carried to its utmost perfection by the present Inspector General
> —which perfection consists in employing some other person, gener-
> ally the Deputy Inspector in Chief, to give evidence about something
> which in no wise concerns him, and to collect the evidence of order-
> lies. I am sorry that the Inspector General has injured me, that it
> prevents me from taking up the medical officers' quarrel, for fear it
> might be thought my own.

There were some medical officers, however, who thought that
Miss Nightingale and some of her supporters were guilty of exaggeration. It has generally been assumed that there was but one side
to the question. Owing to the kindness of Lieutenant-General
Drummond, however, I have been allowed access to some letters
written home by a young Scot named David Gregg, who travelled
out to the Crimea in the same boat as Miss Nightingale, and who
lived in the Barrack Hospital near Miss Nightingale's quarters. His
letters have, so far as I am aware, never previously been published.
The first was written from the Scutari Barrack Hospital and was
dated 30 December 1854. In it occurred the following passage—

> By the bye, if you look in the *Illustrated London News* for 16 Dec. you
> will see a view of a part of Scutari Hospital; it is one of the passages
> and the view is taken from the door of Miss Nightingale's quarters,

just where I live. The picture is not good but will give you some idea of the place. The passage is not nearly so high nor so broad; in the centre between the two rows of beds we have only two or three feet, while in the picture you would think it was eight or ten. You see the first arch crossing over the passage, well, on the right hand side you see a fellow entering or just about to enter a door, you may say that is me for he is going into my quarters. The beds are placed close to our doors and of course all the moaning of the patients at nights is heard to the best advantage while we are in bed; in general however I sleep so sound that that never disturbs me in the least.

You asked me, by the bye, about Miss Nightingale—when on board the *Vectis* I did not know who or what she was, but since then we all know her very well. She is a very kind lady, and what is more has £8000 [*sic*] a year which we all joke about here. The nurses are all under her charge; sometimes we get a visit from her in the wards and if a nurse is required for a patient she sends one. At some parts of the hospital they attend every day and dress the patients, but to do that at all the hospitals would require fifty times the number. She keeps strict watch over them and they work very well, but I think just the same could be done by the orderlies which we have already in our wards. (Soldiers who act as nurses)

I had a farce with Miss Nightingale today; she was visiting some of my patients who were very bad and was asking one poor fellow who had got his leg shot off if he would like rice-water or barley water to drink; he thought for a while and then said he would prefer brandy and water if it was the same to her.

Mr David Gregg left the Barrack Hospital and was posted to Koulali, whence on 27 July 1855 he sent home a letter containing the following passage—

In the *Courier* of 11 July which I have just received I am sorry to see a letter extracted from *The Times* headed 'Neglect of the Wounded in the Crimea,' on the 18th of June. I am sorry to see such a letter as I can tell you it is a lie from beginning to end and calculated not only to alarm the good folks at home but to hurt the service itself.—I lived longer in Scutari Hospital than Mr Stafford and I must say I never saw what he describes. The gentleman who writes the present article must either be mad or a most consummate fool, and ought to be drummed out of the service to the 'rogue's march'. He said he could not get drinking cups, water, food, splints, etc. Why? Because he was an ass and did not know where to get them as he should have done. I have never yet applied in vain for anything which would be of use to my patients, even to calf's foot jelly, lemon jelly, soups, turtle soup or even champagne. Everything can be got if you go the right way about it.

In reading this letter one must remember that it does not invalidate the well authenticated evidence of mismanagement, but it does at least show that matters were not everywhere quite as bad as they were depicted.

Further evidence on this question exists in the library of the R.A.M.C. College at Millbank. By the kindness of the authorities of the College I have been permitted to see and quote from a letter sent home to his parents by Assistant Surgeon Arthur Henry Taylor, who wrote a letter at the time when complaints about the Barrack Hospital were being made. His description was written from a first-hand knowledge of the hospital. The letter is dated 2 January 1855, at a time when matters were at their worst, and the relevant part runs as follows—

I went to Scutari to see the grand hospital there and was greatly pleased with the comfort of the men and arrangements, and astonished at the extent and excellence of the accommodation afforded. The men are placed in long galleries with wards off them and all are clean and well ventilated. It was the grand barracks of the Sultan's troops; along the walls are fixed well-made racks for arms. As a barracks its arrangements are very good and deserve credit. It is the only good thing I have seen in Turkey. As a hospital it is nearly perfect as can be imagined when its extent and hasty adoption for the purpose is considered. However, unfortunately at present fever of a bad type has made its appearance and has carried off many men.

I did not see Miss Nightingale herself but I met several others of the 'sympathizers' as we call them. They all dress in plain black woollen dresses with unbleached linen aprons and a scarf across the shoulders from right to left embroidered in red thread with the words 'Scutari Hospital'; it gives them quite a martial uniform appearance. They all go about slip-shod and very meek looking but evidently proud of their office. The M.O.'s say they are very kind and do a great deal of good but are very much in the way.

The unsatisfactory sanitary state of the hospitals at Scutari, the public outcry in the newspapers, the questions raised in Parliament, not to mention the private representations sent to Sidney Herbert by Miss Nightingale, led to the appointment of a Sanitary Commission which was sent out to report on conditions at the seat of war. By instructions dated 19 February 1855 the Commissioners were authorized 'to inspect every part of such infirmaries, ascertain the character and sufficiency of the drainage and ventilation, the quantity and quality of the water supply, and determine whether the condition of whole is such as to allow by purity of the air and freedom from over-crowding fair play and full scope to medical and surgical treatment for the recovery of health.' The members of the Commission were Dr John Sutherland, Dr Hector Gavin, and Mr Robert Rawlinson. Dr Sutherland was the medical sanitary expert, and it was during the carrying out of his duties in connection with the Commission that he became acquainted with Miss Nightingale. Miss Nightingale must have been able and very willing to supply a lot of useful information to the Commissioners, who found it difficult to criticize the sanitary conditions of the hospitals without implicating the chief medical officer, Dr (afterwards Sir John) Hall, and the Director-General of the Army Medical Service, Sir Andrew Smith.

MISS NIGHTINGALE AND DR HALL

There is no doubt that Miss Nightingale regarded Dr Hall as typical of the system which had broken down under the strain of war, and Dr Hall on his part regarded Miss Nightingale as an interloper who was in some respects undermining his authority. There was truth in both points of view.

Nearly all, if not all of the published accounts of the medical muddle in the Crimea blame and sometimes abuse Dr Hall, but give very little attention to his side of the question. It is true that he may have resented her coming with the powerful backing of the War Office to support her; it is likely also that he may have disparaged her work and tried to keep her out of the hospitals in the Crimea. It must be remembered, however, that she on her side, though careful to submit to Army discipline, was regularly sending long confidential reports to the Minister at War in which she criticized in the most severe terms the sanitary condition of the

3. Corridor adjoining Miss Nightingale's quarters in Barrack Hospital, Scutari

(From 'The Illustrated London News', 1854)

4. Sir John Hall, Inspector-General of Hospitals in Crimea

(From a photograph in 'The Life and Letters of Sir John Hall', by S. M. Mitra)

hospitals, the cooking and the distribution of food, and the availability of supplies—all of which criticisms reflected gravely upon the principal medical officer. He could not know the details of the charges against him, and in any case could not at that time publish any defence. It was something of a paradox that one who denounced the secret reports on junior medical officers should send home to the Minister very serious critical reports which indirectly could not but reflect on the principal medical officer.

Dr Hall visited the hospitals at Scutari only once, just after the battle of Alma, and the report that he sent home to the Director-General—that the hospitals were in as good a state as could possibly be expected—was held up to scorn and ridicule by Miss Nightingale, who first saw those hospitals when they were put to an unprecedented test soon after the battle of Inkerman. Hall was a doctor of the old school who had been in the Army forty-two years. The Director-General of that time explained 'that he was appointed because he happened to be the senior deputy-inspector-general in the Service; a man who had been principal medical officer during four or five years of the Kaffir War; a man of high professional acquirements, of great power of observation, and of highly cultivated intellect; a man who as far as he was a professional man, universally respected and esteemed by the whole Army.'

When the call came for him to go to the seat of war Dr Hall was in India. He was first sent to Varna in Bulgaria, an unhealthy place where the Army was first disembarked. There was already much sickness among the troops. When the move to Scutari was decided upon he was not given due notice of the expected move and, in the consequent muddle, the medical transport and much of the medical stores which were intended for the hospitals at Scutari were lost or left behind. This confusion, which appears to have been outside Dr Hall's control, was mainly responsible for the lack of many of the essential medical requirements at Scutari.

According to modern standards Dr Hall might be accounted incompetent, but according to the standards of that time he would

4

merit a less severe judgement. It was his misfortune that the cast-iron system of administration in which he was involved was subjected to criticism by one who had a greater knowledge of civil hospitals than anyone else then living; one, moreover, who had never previously come into contact with the unforeseen and often unforeseeable accidents and catastrophes of war.

The system of army administration at that time precluded any action except through the recognized channels. Junior officers could not do anything other than their routine duties, and even the principal medical officer had little executive power outside his strictly medical duties. Even the sites for hospitals were not, as a rule, permitted to be chosen by him, and he had the greatest difficulty in getting necessary alterations made to buildings. Hall did not choose the sites of the Scutari hospitals. The whole system of administration, though it might function tolerably well in peacetime, was not elastic enough to meet a war emergency, and the Crimean campaign proved this. We believe that everyone who has studied the documents connected with the Crimean muddle will agree with the considered judgement of Sir Edward Cook—

> To me, after much reading of the documents, it seems that Dr Hall was the victim of a false position. He had been appointed medical inspector-general in the Crimea when he was still in India and he did not arrive on the scene in time to think out the preparations properly. Miss Nightingale never allowed personal feelings to affect the impartiality of her judgements. Dr Hall disputed her authority and resented her interference. She fought him and in the end she beat him; but there are passages in her letters which bear testimony to his good services and high capacity in many respects. Nor were their personal relations unfriendly; but she saw in him throughout an antagonistic influence.

The Report of the Sanitary Commission, written by Dr Sutherland, made no charge against the medical department of the Army and, as it was stated in the report, 'desired to allot blame to no-one.' Nevertheless, Dr Hall not unnaturally took many of the criticisms as applying to himself and he therefore published a reply. This was answered by Dr Sutherland, which led to a second pamphlet by Dr Hall in which he summed up his own position with regard to the findings of the Commission—

> With these advantages at their command, and knowing how little they really accomplished, and with what difficulty they accomplished that little, one might have thought they would have had more consideration for their brethren of the military profession who were less fortunately situated, and whose powers were limited to recommendations which had to be regulated by the exigencies of the service and consideration from those in command.

There is substance in this rejoinder.

Considerable misunderstanding, if not ill-will, between Dr Hall and Miss Nightingale arose from the ambiguity of her instructions from the War Office. She had consented to accept the office of 'Superintendent of the female nursing establishment in the English military hospitals in Turkey,' and her detailed instructions were as follows—

> You will, on your arrival there, place yourself at once in communication with the Chief Medical Officer of the hospital at Scutari, under whose orders and direction you will carry on the duties of your appointment. Everything relating to the distribution of the nurses, the hours of their attendance, their allotment to particular duties is placed in your hands, subject of course to the sanction and approval of the Chief Medical Officer.

These were wide powers but limited by the words 'in Turkey.' Strictly speaking her authority would not extend to the Crimea. Early in 1856 she made a formal complaint to Lord Panmure about the posting of two nurses to a hospital in the Crimea, which posting was, according to her information, sanctioned by Sir John Hall without consulting her. Lord Panmure, who had sent out Colonel Lefroy to report privately to him on the state of affairs, on Lefroy's advice issued a General Order defining once and for all Miss Nightingale's position. The General Order was conveyed to Sir William Codrington on a communication dated 25 February 1856. It ran as follows—

> It has been intimated to the Secretary of State for War that female nurses have been introduced into one of the hospitals of the Army in

the East by the medical authorities without the concurrence of the Lady Superintendent of the Female Nursing Establishment. His Lordship has addressed the following despatch to the Commander of the Forces, with a desire that it should be promulgated in General Orders:

It appears to me that the Medical authorities of the Army do not correctly comprehend Miss Nightingale's position as it has been officially recognized by me. I therefore think it right to state to you briefly for their guidance, as well as for the information of the Army, what the position of that excellent lady is. Miss Nightingale is recognized by Her Majesty's Government as the General Superintendent of the female nursing establishment of the military Hospitals of the Army.

No lady, or sister, or nurse, is to be transferred into any hospital without consultation with her. Her instructions, however, require to have the approval of the Principal Medical Officer in the exercise of the responsibility thus vested in her.

The Principal Medical Officer will communicate with Miss Nightingale upon all subjects connected with the Female Nursing Establishment, and will give his directions through that lady.

It should be noted that this order was made, ostensibly, because of a complaint made by Miss Nightingale. When the Order was promulgated Sir John at once made a dignified reply.

Headquarters Camp. Crimea.

March 12, 1856.

In returning Lord Panmure's despatch of the 25th February, 1856, No. 170, in which His Lordship states that 'his attention has been called by Miss Nightingale to the circumstances of two female nurses having been recently introduced by the Principal Medical Officer in the Crimea into the Monastery Hospital without any previous communication with that lady, who alone is recognized by Her Majesty's Government as having the supervision of the Female Nursing Establishment at the seat of war, and I have to direct that you will call the attention of Sir John Hall to the irregularity of this proceeding, and at the same time will guard against its recurrence by promulgating in General Orders the rightful position of Miss Nightingale.'

I trust I may be permitted to state, for the information of the Secretary of State for War, that I never appointed any nurses to the Monastery Hospital, although I was invited to do so by Miss Nightingale's own letter of the 27th October 1855, a copy of which, with my reply, is annexed; and what is more to the purpose, every nurse that either

now is, or ever has been employed there was sent up from Scutari by
Miss Nightingale herself, as you will observe by the following documents which were given to me by Miss Wear, the superintendent.

(Then follows a list of relevant notes and memoranda.)

The position of Miss Nightingale will now be perfectly understood
by the medical officers of the Army, but it is right I should add that,
until the present time, I have never received from the authorities at
home any official instructions defining her exact powers and authority, as it was generally understood that her mission related solely to
the hospitals at Scutari; and until the receipt of the present communication from the Secretary of State for War, I should not have thought
that I was exceeding the authority of my situation, as head of the
medical department, of this Army, in appointing on an emergency
two nurses to a military hospital; but even that trifling act of authority, I beg distinctly to state, I have not exercised on the present occasion, and the only thing I can charge my memory with having done
that could give even a colour to this accusation is having, when Miss
Wear was in tribulation about someone to accompany her to the
Monastery, sanctioned the Purveyor writing down to Smyrna to
inquire if two nurses could be maintained there. An answer from
Mr Fitzgerald in the negative was obtained. Subsequently, I understood, when the Smyrna establishment was ordered to be reduced,
that two nurses were sent up from there to Miss Nightingale at
Scutari, but I am not answerable for that.

Having been censured by the Secretary of State on information
that is not correct, I request that you will do me the honour to
submit this my explanation, which I trust will be satisfactory to his
Lordship.

Sir John's explanation seems reasonable.[1] Shortly after this Miss
Nightingale wrote to Sir John asking a question about some requisitions. Sir John's reply was formal but dignified, although at the
time he must have been smarting under the false accusation and the
humiliating censure from the War Department. If his explanation
be correct, the fault was not with him but with the nursing establishment. The reply ran as follows (March 26 1856)—

I am favoured with your letter of yesterday's date informing me of
the arrival of the first instalment of nurses for the Land Transport

[1] The letters are printed in the *Life of Sir John Hall*, by S. M. Mitra.

Hospital, and requesting to know whether I wish the requisitions on the Purveyor to be countersigned by the Principal Medical Officer. All requisitions for the personal use of the nurses the Purveyor has orders to comply with at once on your, or any Superintendent's demand. But it is the usage in military hospitals for all demands for the sick to be made by the Medical Officer in charge, with the approval of his immediate superior, and I should wish this rule to be pursued in the Land Transport as it is in the other hospitals. It insures uniformity and exactness in the hospital expenditure accounts, while the wants of the sick are duly cared for, both of which are very desirable in military hospital economy.

With regard to the nurses at the General Hospital, Balaklava, the supervision of whom you state has been reimposed on you by the War Department, I take leave to observe that all doubt has now been removed by the General Order as to your relative positions, and it is a question, not for me, but for Mrs Bridgeman to decide, but in justice to her and the Sisters under her orders I must state that they have given me the most perfect satisfaction by the quiet and efficient manner in which they have performed their duty since they have been employed there, and I should regret their departure.

When on 11 April 1856 Mrs Bridgeman and her Sisters left for England, their places were supplied by Miss Nightingale by nurses from Scutari without previously consulting Sir John Hall. In answer to Miss Nightingale's letter telling him what she had done, Sir John replied as follows (April 15th 1856)—

As the Army is on the eve of breaking up and vacating the Crimea I regret that I was not previously made acquainted with your intention of withdrawing nurses from Scutari, where they will soon be more required than here. This unnecessary move may, I fear, have put them to inconvenience and the public to expense without any adequate advantage from the arrangement.

Still another letter of complaint came from Miss Nightingale a few days later. This time it was something to do with the nurses' diet. Sir John replied with a clear explanation.

In reply to your letter of the 19th inst. in which you complain of the nurses at the General Hospital not having received certain articles of their full diet ration, I beg to inform you that I caused the matter to be inquired into at once, and I now take leave to forward you copies of letters of explanation from Mr Fitzgerald and Mr Powell, by whom you will observe the fault is attributed to your own servant, who declined to receive the articles you allude to oftener than once a week; but if you will be kind enough to give him instructions to receive them, they will be issued to him daily, or in any other way that you may find convenient and agreeable to yourself and the nurses.

In none of these letters does Sir John allow any rancour to show, although he must have felt very sore. Only to his wife did he reveal the depth of feeling which he managed to hide so well under formal language. Soon after the promulgation of the General Order he wrote to Lady Hall as follows—

> I am quite prostrated, as the General Order, procured by mendacity, has deprived me of the only real nurses we have ever had, for Mrs Bridgeman, a very superior and conscientious person, the Mother Superior of the Sisters of Charity, has positively refused to acknowledge Miss Nightingale's authority, and I cannot blame her after what is past, and they will all go home on Saturday next. Thus the Government loses the free services of these estimable women, and the soldiers the benefit of their ministration, to gratify Miss Nightingale.
>
> I was told, when I declined to interfere, that right or wrong, Miss Nightingale's friends were powerful enough to carry her through. My reply was 'So much the greater pity.'

This private note of Sir John's compares favourably with some of the confidential remarks about Sir John made by his redoubtable antagonist.

SIR JOHN HALL AND THE DIRECTOR-GENERALSHIP OF THE ARMY MEDICAL SERVICE

At the end of the Crimean War it was known that the Director-General of the Army Medical Service, Sir Andrew Smith, would be due to retire shortly. Miss Nightingale knew that there was a probability that Sir John Hall might be nominated for the position, and she thought (most likely correctly) that he would probably oppose many of the reforms which she thought ought to be introduced. She therefore used all her influence and persuasive powers to prevent this appointment and noted as one of the points gained in her interview with Lord Panmure: 'Sir John Hall not to be made

Director-General while Lord Panmure in office.' The report of the
Royal Commission on the Sanitary State of the Army appeared in
February 1858, and soon afterwards the Government was defeated
and General Peel was made Minister of War. Miss Nightingale
therefore spoke to Sidney Herbert, who, at her request, interviewed General Peel, who promised 'to make no appointment
nor to take any steps in regard to the Medical Department or
sanitary measures till he had conferred with me.' Later Mr
Herbert wrote to Dr Sutherland: 'Please tell Miss Nightingale that
I warned Peel against the expected recommendation of Sir J.
Hall and he will I think be prepared to turn a deaf ear to it. I wrote
yesterday to him about another subject and threw in some praise
of Alexander.' On June 11 1858 Dr T. Alexander (Miss Nightingale's nominee) was appointed Director-General on the retirement
of Sir Andrew Smith. Reform was now assured and Sir John Hall
had again been defeated.

SIR JOHN HALL AND THE ROYAL COMMISSION
ON THE SANITARY STATE OF THE ARMY

Sir John Hall gave evidence before the Royal Commission which
was appointed to inquire into the sanitary conditions of the Army.
Most of the members of the Commission were supporters of Miss
Nightingale, and she herself had the greatest part in choosing who
should be asked to give evidence, and what questions should be
put to them. She was indeed practically indirectly cross-exami-
ning in the presence of a sympathetic jury. From papers that are
available it is clear that Sidney Herbert tried to persuade her to be
lenient, and that for a moment she was almost persuaded. In a
letter dated 3 July 1857 she wrote to Sir John McNeill and
included this comment—

> I am quite as well aware as he [Sidney Herbert] can be that it is
> inexpedient and even unprincipled to go back now into past delin-
> quencies. What is more I feel for him who was victimized by a sys-
> tem of which he could know nothing until the results appeared. It
> is easy for me to be wise after the fact, me, who saw the results.

But other thoughts intervened and once more she hardened—

But it would be untrue and unconscientious for me to give evidence upon an indifferent matter like that of hospital construction, leaving untouched the great matters which will affect (and have affected) the mortality of our sick and wounded more than any mere architecture could do.

Miss Nightingale, in her preparation for the evidence of Sir John Hall, wrote to Sir John McNeill asking for some hints which might help in the questioning of Hall. She made it clear what sort of help she wished for by adding—

I would only recall to your memory the long series of proofs—his incredible apathy, . . . to my mind with the exception of G., the worst of the liars.

It may be that she relented somewhat before the time of the actual examination, for Dr Sutherland was not present on that occasion and nothing important was elicited from Hall's evidence. After his evidence Miss Nightingale commented (in a letter to McNeill)—

Sir J. Hall's evidence fell harmless. It broke down utterly from want of truthfulness and perpetual doubling.

The fact of the matter was that Sir John Hall was already a broken man, broken by events over which (as Miss Nightingale herself agreed) he had little or no control. He retired on half-pay and died in Pisa on 17 January 1866. The force of events, public clamour and private intrigue were too much for him.

4

The Medical Members
of the Sanitary Commission

MISS NIGHTINGALE RETURNED from the Crimea filled, nay almost inspired, with a firm resolve to remedy some of the abuses she had so clearly seen in the working of the Army Medical Service. Nursing played but a small part in this. Sanitation was a considerable part. Special education of the medical officers in the Service took a leading place in her scheme, but what she would have liked to do, and went a long way towards doing, was to recast the whole administration of the Army Medical Service. She was not a public politician, but worked by influencing those statesmen who were in a position to get things done. Immediately on her return she succeeded in obtaining the sympathy and moral support of Queen Victoria and the Prince Consort. She then had an interview with Lord Panmure, persuaded him of the need for the appointment of a Royal Commission to investigate the sanitary state of the Army, and discussed with him who should be members of that Commission. Prior to this she had consulted her medical friends, Dr Sutherland and Sir John McNeill, who advised her as to the best names to suggest and the instructions on which they should be asked to act. When she interviewed Lord Panmure, therefore, she was well prepared. The interview took place on 16 November 1856, and, as with all her interviews, Miss Nightingale made notes as to what passed during the discussion. These notes have been printed *in extenso* in Sir E. Cook's biography of Miss Nightingale, for, he says, they are so 'characteristic of her humour.' They are more than that. They show her knowledge of the character of the doctors she was discussing, and, still more, they serve to reveal the quick reactions and intelligent workings of her keen and

acute mind when pitted against an experienced statesman. She
obviously enjoyed the combat of wits, and the reader must judge
whose wit was the brighter. The notes she made were clearly
meant for Sidney Herbert to read.

(Nov. 16) My 'Pan' here for three hours. Wrote down—

      ⎧ President. Mr Herbert
      ⎨ General Storks   Jury
      ⎩ Colonel Lefroy

      ⎧ Dr A. Smith
      ⎨ Dr McLachlan   Army Doctors
      ⎩ Dr Brown

      ⎧ Dr Sutherland
      ⎨ Dr Martin   Civil Doctors
      ⎩ Dr Farr

          Secretary.   Dr Balfour.   Army Doctor

Will have Drs balanced. Not fair: two soldiers reckon as against
civil element. Whenever I represented it (I did not know old 'Pan'
was so sharp) he offered to take off Colonel Lefroy! so I had to
knock under.

Won't bring back Alexander from Canada. Will have three Army
doctors. So, like a sensible general in retreat I named (Dr Joseph)
Brown, Surgeon Major Grenadier Guards, therefore not wedded to
Dr Smith, an old Peninsular and Reformer. Left Lord P. his McLach-
lan, who will do less harm than a better man. He has generously
struck out Milton. Seeing him in such a 'coming on' disposition I
was so good as to leave him Dr Smith, the more so as I could not
help it.

Have a tough fight for it: Dr Balfour as Secretary. Pan amazed
at my condescension in naming a military doctor; so I concealed the
fact of the man being a dangerous animal and obstinate innovator.
Failed in one point. Unfairly. Pan told Sir J. Clark he was to be on
Won't have him now. Sir J. Clark has become interested. Agreeable
to the Queen to have him—just as well to have Her on our side as
she has done us mischief in re Tulloch. An enlightened man, a very
timid man, personal friend of Smith's.

Besides things Ld P. finds convenient to forget, has really incon-
veniently bad memory as to names, facts, dates, and numbers. Hope
I know what discipline is too well, having had the honour of holding
H.M. Commission, to have a better memory than my chief. Pan has

four Army doctors, really, therefore according to his principle I have a right to four civilians.

Instructions: general and comprehensive, comprising the whole Army Medical Department, and the health of the Army, at home and abroad. Semi-official letter from Secretary of State in Memorandum from President giving details. Smith, equal parts lachrymose and threatening, will say, 'I did not understand that we were to inquire into this.'

My master jealous. Does not wish it to be supposed he takes suggestions from me, which crime indeed very unjust to impute to him. You must drag it through. If not you, no one else.

(1) Col. Lefroy to be instructed by Lord P. to draw up scheme for Army Medical School, appendix to his own Military Education. *I won.*

(2) Netley Hospital plans to be privately reported on by Sutherland and me to Lord P.   *I won.*

(3) Commissariat to be put on same footing as India.   *I lost.*

(4) Camp at Aldershot to 'do' for themselves—kill cattle, bake bread, build, drain, shoe-make, tailor etc. Lord P. will consider: quite agrees: means 'will do nothing.'

(5) Sir J. Hall not to be made Director-General while Lord P. in office.   *I won.*

(6) Colonel Tulloch to be knighted. *I lost* (unless I can make Col. T. accept an agreement, which I shan't.)

(7) About Statistics, Lord P. said (i) the strength of these regiments averaged only 200, (ii) denied the mortality, (iii) said that statistics prove anything. And I, as soldier, must not know better than my Chief.

(8) Lord P. contradicted everything—so that I retain the most sanguine expectations of success.

In the final list of Commissioners Mr Stafford (a friend of Miss Nightingale) took the place of Colonel Lefroy, but Sir James Clark came in instead of Dr Brown, and, best of all, for the reformers, Dr Alexander was brought back from Canada to join the Commission. Sir T. Phillips was the lawyer member. Six of the nine members and four out of the five medical members were entirely sympathetic with Miss Nightingale's ideas, and the medical secretary of the Commission, Dr Graham Balfour, was also her supporter. Sir Andrew Smith, the Director-General, was the single 'die-hard' medical member.

This is a suitable place to say a few words about those two medical members of the Commission who are not more fully described elsewhere in this book.

Dr (afterwards Sir) Ranald Martin was one of the men whose ideas had been considerably influenced by his discussions with Miss Nightingale. At that time he was sixty-four years of age. He had served in India as a surgeon in the service of the East India Company and was an authority on the diseases of India and on sanitary matters. On his return to England he had been appointed Inspector-General of Army hospitals. He was the friend and medical adviser of Lord Macaulay. He wrote the article on 'Hospitals' in Holmes's *System of Surgery*, and Miss Nightingale must have known that his views on sanitation largely corresponded with her own.

Dr Graham Balfour, who was appointed secretary to the Commission, was forty-four years old when he first became acquainted with Miss Nightingale. He was born in 1813, and studied medicine at Edinburgh University, where he took his doctorate of medicine in 1834. Two years later he entered the Army, where, almost from the start of his career, he was engaged in the statistical branch. Miss Nightingale must have heard of his skill in this subject and of his sympathy with proposals for reform in the Army Medical Service, for, as related above, it was at her suggestion that he was appointed secretary to the Commission. When the instructions for the Commission were finally agreed upon she wrote to him as follows—

> I send you enclosed what was finally decided upon this morning, as to names and instructions. If some slip does not yet come between our cup and our lips it will receive the Queen's signature on Friday week. But Dr Smith has not yet seen it and my Lord is, as I have often found, the most bully-able of mortals. Every one of the members of the Commission has been carried by force of will against Dr A. Smith, and poor Pan has been the shuttlecock.—You will see curious traces of the struggle to exclude and the struggle to include all Reform in the progress of the MS.—I think I am not without merit for labouring at bullying Pan, which is a pretty kind of warfare, very unpleasant.

As secretary, Graham Balfour had a great deal to do with the actual production of the report which appeared in February 1858. He sent an early copy to Miss Nightingale, which promptly elicited from her a congratulatory note—

> I have not been able to thank you yet for your great work which I received on the 2nd. I admire him very much. I think he looks handsome, and I cannot help congratulating you on the successful conclusion of this part of your labours.

She added: 'Lady Tulloch says I make my pillow of Blue-books. It certainly has been the case with this.' She made a similar statement in another letter a little later—

> I remember hearing one of the cleverest women I ever knew—and a good historical writer herself—say that a full chronicle of dry dates was to her the most interesting, the most fascinating of all reading. I am conscious of the same feeling in reading a column of dry and statistical figures.

The Royal Commission recommended that four sub-commissions should be set up, one of which should deal with statistics. The statistical sub-commission reported in 1858, and thereafter a reorganized statistical branch of the Army Medical Department was instituted with Dr Graham Balfour in charge of it. He had the rank of Deputy Inspector-General. This statistical department issued annual reports on the health of the Army in which Miss Nightingale took great interest and concerning which she was sometimes very critical. In January 1861 she complained to Graham Balfour that he drew unnecessary conclusions from the statistics instead of letting the figures speak for themselves. He replied—

> As to your objection—I do not think that you can entirely separate causation of disease from statistics—at least if you do you make them a dry mass of figures that will be looked at by none but numeromaniacs.

A few days later she replied with a rather severe criticism of the report. She told him 'the drier, the better,' and after several strictures ended with the words, 'you will think me very disagreeable.' He took this in good part and answered amicably: 'I have always had a strong liking for the people who are classed as disagreeable—as you place yourself in that category, of course you enrol yourself among my favourites.'

They were both interested in and concerned with the International Statistical Congress which was held in London in 1860. Graham Balfour was appointed secretary of one of the sections of the Congress, but for some unknown reason he was not informed in proper time of the place of the meetings. He was very annoyed and was inclined to make a fuss about it. Miss Nightingale heard of his intention and succeeded in calming his wrath by writing him a letter which was a masterpiece of tact—

> You are quite right in what you say. We are all of us in the same boat. And if it were not that England *would not be* the mercantile nation she *is*, if she had not business habits somewhere, I should wonder from my experience where they are. Certain of us were asked to do business this morning, and to have it ready by tonight, which if not done would arrest the proceedings of the Congress, and if done must be the fruit of only five hours consideration, when five months might just as well have been granted for it. I don't say that this is so bad as the treatment of you who are secretary. But still it is provoking to see a great international business worked in this way.
>
> What I want now is to put a good face upon it before the foreigners. Let them not see our shortcomings and disunions. Many countries far behind us in political business, are far before us in political power.— I hope that you will try to impress these foreign delegates then, with a sense of *our* 'enormous business power' (in which I don't believe one bit) and to keep the Congress going. Many thanks for all your papers. I trust you will settle some sectional business with the delegates here tomorrow morning. And I trust that I shall be able to see you, if not tomorrow morning, soon.
>
> Mind, I don't mean anything against your Office by this tirade. On the contrary, I believe it is one of the few efficient ones now in existence.

There can be little doubt that such a letter achieved its object. Though the correspondence between the two friends continued for many years it was not voluminous. Graham Balfour continued to send Miss Nightingale his annual statistical reports. In 1872 the reception of the report drew from her an interesting reply—

> Let me say in the first place that the Report is the best you have yet issued—and that for practical information on Army medical matters

it stands alone. . . . The superior way in which the recruiting work has been done by the Army medical officers in most creditable to them. . . . indeed the reforms instituted by Sidney Herbert have already placed the Army Medical Department at the top of the medical profession. And the improvement is still going on. God be praised for it. And you all! . . .

This makes my excuse for letting the poor word serve to express what I always remember when I write or hear from you. Our fifteen years of friendship began under Sidney Herbert, and none the less strong on my side because interrupted by long sickness, etc.

Four years after this (in 1876) Dr Graham Balfour retired with the rank of surgeon-general. He died in 1891, a few months before the death of Dr John Sutherland.

5

The Doctor
Miss Nightingale championed

SIR JOHN McNEILL (1795–1883)

Sir John McNeill was a doctor whom Miss Nightingale admired and almost venerated. In none of her innumerable letters did she ever speak of him with other than laudatory terms, and there is no doubt that she had the utmost respect for his character and judgement. Sir John was already a distinguished man when first he met Miss Nightingale. He was a Highlander born at Colonsay in 1795, and he received his education at St Andrews and Edinburgh Universities. Qualifying at Edinburgh in 1816, he married, and entered the service of the East India Company as an assistant surgeon. After four years spent in India (chiefly on active service), he was sent to Teheran in the capacity of surgeon to the British Chargé d'Affaires in Persia. His ability, common sense and character soon made it clear that he possessed qualities useful in diplomatic work and he was appointed Assistant Chargé d'Affaires. In course of time he was entrusted with many delicate diplomatic missions, all of which he carried out with wisdom and success. In 1839 he was awarded the G.C.B. After spending twenty-four years in Persia he returned home, retired from the service of the East India Company, and in 1845 took the post of Chairman of the Board of Supervision which had been set up to administer the new Poor Law in Scotland.

In the course of his experiences in the Middle East Sir John had acquired a first-hand knowledge of the people, government and resources of Turkey, Persia, and the adjoining countries. When therefore in 1854 there was a great popular outcry about the mis-management in the Crimea, and the Government wished to placate its critics by a thorough and impartial investigation of the causes which had led to this state of affairs, it was natural that Sir John should be one of those called upon to undertake the mission. He was then sixty years old, but still vigorous and in full posses-sion of his powers. On 12 February 1855 he was summoned by telegram to London, where he and Colonel Tulloch were authorized to proceed to Scutari and the Crimea 'to inquire into the whole arrangement and management of the Commissariat Department.' They were also asked to inquire into the alleged delay in unshipping and distributing the clothes and other stores. They were given large powers to summon and examine witnesses and to require the production of all necessary books and papers, and to make any suggestions for improvement to Lord Raglan and to the Minister for War. Their inquiries were to deal with provisions, forage, clothing, and the means of transport of such articles.

This was a very delicate mission, for it entailed the close examination of military officers by commissioners, one of whom was a civilian and the other an officer junior in rank to many of those who were to be questioned. Nevertheless, under the wise guidance of Sir John, a very thorough investigation was made, two hundred witnesses were questioned, and not only was the evidence of each witness written down, but each person exam-ined was asked to read through the transcript of his evidence and to sign it in token of his acceptance of the record as correct. This left little room for error. Sir John throughout the report did not include any criticism of any particular person, but merely stated the facts, which were allowed to speak for them-selves. His colleague Colonel Tulloch would have been more outspoken if he had not been restrained by his older and wiser colleague.

During the course of their inquiry the Commissioners met Miss Nightingale at Scutari, and from the first she recognized the sterling character of Sir John, and even consulted him medically. In May 1855, on leaving the Crimea, he wrote to her—

MY DEAR MISS NIGHTINGALE

I hope that although the circumstances which led you to apply to me had no reality, the confidence which you extended to me was real, and I can sincerely assure you that it will always give me great satisfaction to find an opportunity of proving to you that it has not been misplaced.

The friendship thus begun continued for nearly thirty years. The two commissioners conducted their investigations during the months of March, April, and May, 1855, and they completed the first part of their report in June, but the second part was not finished for another six months. It was presented to the Minister and to Parliament in January 1856 and was then made public. The Press, led by *The Times*, were loud in praise of the report, which confirmed that there had been gross mismanagement. Although it did not specifically blame any particular officers, it mentioned several to whom blame might easily be assigned. The natural result would have been for the Government to take some action, and at the very least thank the Commissioners for so efficiently carrying out their arduous task. But no such action was taken, for two factors militated against it.

In the first place the high officers who were mentioned strongly resented the implications involved, and therefore in the House of Lords they attacked the Government for publishing them. On the other hand, in the House of Commons the general opinion was that the officers were blameworthy. The second and more cogent reason could not at that time be made public, for it placed the Prime Minister in a delicate position. The Army was theoretically responsible to the Crown, and the presentation of the report to the House of Commons induced the Queen to write to Lord Palmerston a letter of complaint, in which she stated that 'these officers: . . . find themselves accused under the authority of the Government, and that accusation communicated to the Legislature, without ever having been heard in answer or allowed an opportunity to defend themselves.' The Queen continued: 'It is quite

evident that if matters are left so, and military officers of the Queen's
Army are to be judged as to the manner in which they have
discharged their military duties by a Committee of the House of
Commons, the Command of the Army is at once transferred from
the Crown to that Assembly.' The Queen approved of the suggestion made by Sir James Graham that a military commission should
be appointed to look into the matter. It is possible that the Queen
did not know that all the evidence relating to the officers mentioned
had in fact been submitted to them for their signature for confirm-
ation, and that they had not impugned its accuracy.

It has been justly observed concerning the Government's action
that 'the choice was forced upon them [the Cabinet] of upholding
their own commissioners by assuming an attitude hostile to the
Army and displeasing to the Crown, or of denouncing the report
of their own Commission, facing hostile motions in the House
of Commons, while satisfying "those in high places" and the
Army.'[1] In consequence of these factors the Government took up
an attitude which to the general public appeared unfair, not to say
ungrateful to the Commissioners, who had performed a difficult
task remarkably well.

In accordance with the Queen's wishes a Board of General
Officers was appointed to investigate the 'animadversions' which
were stated to have been made in the report against certain officers.
The Board sat at Chelsea, and was composed of senior officers none
of whom had served in the Crimean war. The House of Commons
at that time passed no resolution of thanks to Sir John McNeill and
Colonel Tulloch, but by their appointing a special Board they
almost seemed to put the Commissioners themselves on trial as to
the accuracy of their report. Though Lord Palmerston said that the
Government felt 'much obliged to these gentlemen for the able
and satisfactory manner in which they have performed the duties
they undertook' it was generally felt that they had been slighted.
The two Commissioners reacted very differently to this apparent
slight. Sir John, though very puzzled at the absence of public
acknowledgement of their services, remained calm and aloof and

---

[1] *Life of Sir John McNeill*, page 358.

made no public complaint. Colonel Tulloch, though advised by Sir John to take no part in the Chelsea inquiry, appeared before the Board and justified the report, but it caused him much anxiety and he suffered a physical breakdown in consequence. Apparently no member of the Government explained to the Commissioners the true state of the matter.

The report of the Chelsea Board was published in July 1856 and was found to 'whitewash' all the officers mentioned in the report of the Commissioners, and to attribute all the terrible privations to the lack of forage, which should have been sent out from England.

This nullification of all the work done by McNeill and Tulloch roused indignation all over the country, and in many big towns prominent men of business drew up appreciative addresses which were presented to them thanking them for their great services and expressing sympathy with them in the slight to which they had been subjected.

Miss Nightingale helped to swell the tide of public feeling. In the account given by Sir Edward Cook it is stated that she and her relatives 'did something to advance the movement' of public sympathy. She was deeply stirred by what she thought to be a great act of injustice. Her admiration for Sir John McNeill and her personal knowledge of the mismanagement in the Crimea caused her to do all she could to support the Commissioners. How deeply she felt can be gauged by the following passage which occurs in a letter to Sidney Herbert written in January 1857—

I cannot but earnestly deprecate, and as far as I am myself concerned, resolved entirely to withdraw from the carrying out of that Commission which I believe Lord Panmure supposes himself to have granted at my request.

That she should have for a moment contemplated the giving up of that project upon which, more than anything else, she had set her heart, shows the depth of indignation which stirred her.

In February 1857 the suggestion was made by Lord Palmerston in Parliament that the usual acknowledgement for the rendering of special services might be accorded to the two Commissioners, and through Lord Panmure a gift of one thousand pounds was offered to each of them. Both indignantly refused the offer. On 1 March 1857 Miss Nightingale wrote to Sir John and gave her view as to why Lord Palmerston had spoken in such a restrained manner about their services.—

> The real meaning of what Lord Palmerston said to the House was 'I would make the Crimean Commissioners both Dukes if I could. But I cannot do anything to throw odium upon the Army without displacing myself, and I am not man enough to do that.'

That comment would seem to indicate that the true reason for Lord Palmerston's action was at that time unknown to Miss Nightingale.

When she heard of the monetary offer to the Commissioners her wrath was still further roused. On 20 February she wrote to the wife of Colonel Tulloch expressing indignation at the action of the Government.

> I am glad they have been such fools. I am sure the British Lion will sympathize in this insult, and if it does not, then it is a degraded beast.

Her obvious indignation induced Colonel Tulloch to write to Sir John in the following terms—

> I enclose a letter from Miss Nightingale whom I informed of the offer this evening. You will see how strongly she feels in this matter. I do think a few lines in *The Times* in her own name stating that she blushed for the insult, would have a good effect but I must keep back everything till I hear from you.

McNeill was less excitable and more dignified than his colleague and must have discouraged the proposition made in this letter, for nothing appeared in *The Times* under her name. But she had other, and less obvious ways of influencing statesmen and of achieving her aims. She was at this time in almost daily collaboration with Sidney Herbert over the proposed Sanitary Commission. She must have instilled her views on the McNeill-Tulloch affair deeply on the mind of her friend, for when on 12 March 1857 the question once more came before the House of Commons it was the impassioned speech of Sidney Herbert which induced the House to pass unanimously without a division the following resolution—

> That Sir John McNeill and Colonel Tulloch ably fulfilled the duty entrusted to them of inquiry into the arrangements and management of the Commissariat Department; and that considering the able services rendered by them as Commissioners in the Crimea, and the high testimony in their favour of Her Majesty's Government, an humble address be presented to Her Majesty praying that some special mark of approbation be conferred upon them.

The Minister wrote to Sir John, asking him whether he would prefer a baronetcy or a membership of the Privy Council. He chose the latter, which, of course, entitled him to be addressed as Right Honourable. This called forth from Miss Nightingale the following note—

> MY DEAR SIR JOHN,
>
> I direct my letter with a very great deal of pleasure. I consider that you and Sir Alexander Tulloch have been borne on the arms of the people. The poor Crown has been worsted. But it was not our fault.

It will be noted that she identifies herself with the campaign in favour of the Commissioners. There can be little doubt that her widespread influence, particularly with Sidney Herbert, had a great deal to do with the public honour finally brought to them.

In Kinglake's *History of the Crimean War* there is an account of the McNeill-Tulloch affair which adopted the view taken by the Chelsea Board of Officers. This exasperated Miss Nightingale, who unburdened herself to Sir John McNeill in a characteristic letter (9 April 1881)—

> To tell the truth I have not read, I could not read Mr Kinglake's volume. He sent it me with a very kind note—at least it was meant to be kind, but it was fulsome, (acknowledging my statistics) which I never answered. The book I did not open. To go over all that time again, that time the history of which we had written with our best heart and blood, knowing how I should see it travestied by his opinions, a sort of grotesque or caricature of it, was beyond my strength, overworked and ill as I am. And yet I had no idea to what a degree his misrepresentations had reached till I read your most terse

and able preface to Sir A. Tulloch's book. . . . How little is left of all the good work of 1856 and that five years till 1861 for the Army. . . . The Army Hospitals have sunk back to what they were, the Army Medical School completely ignores the steady strides of the last 20 years of civil life in sanitary things, in hospital administration, in nurse training—But after all we must not judge year by year, day by day and moment by moment—What you have done can never be lost or undone. A million Kinglakes can never shake it. It is as firm as God himself.

Sir John was of great assistance to Miss Nightingale in the preparation of her précis of evidence for the Army Sanitary Commission. In September 1856 she wrote asking him for information about the organization of the Army. She was precise in formulating exactly what she wanted. She asked for information dealing with four distinct branches.

1. The distribution of authority and accountability in military hospitals.
2. The checks on their expenditure.
3. The division of labour.
4. The whole system of Army Medical statistics.

He must have sent her a detailed and excellent account, for three months later she wrote to him: 'Thank you for the ten most valuable memoranda which you have so kindly sent me relating to the government of general army military hospitals. You will see how largely I have borrowed from you.' In another letter she told him that she had included most of his memoranda in her evidence without alteration. He was one of the doctors whose judgement she always respected. In the letter congratulating him on being made a Privy Councillor, she wrote—

I have so little time to write now that I cannot give myself the indulgence of telling you how much good you did me, soul and mind. Yours is another atmosphere from what I am used to. And, reckoning the life of a man at £120, which is my manifestation of spiritualism, if you value your Crimean expedition at the number of lives you have saved and will save in our Army, you may add one more for mine.

When she was completing the précis of her evidence she wrote to him on a point which was worrying her, i.e. whether she should insert the sources of her quotations and references (4 June 1857)—

> The question whether I should put 'chapter and verse' to the quotations is, I think, just as broad as it is long. You know how even educated men will go off upon a word. One does not like the Roebuck Committee, another does not like the Stafford Committee; one distrusts this Commission and another distrusts that, till all thought about the truth is merged in a discussion of authorities. Socrates says something to the effect that nine-tenths of our belief comes from sympathy, antipathy, authority and blind assimilation. I do not know therefore whether to put references or not.

Miss Nightingale frequently consulted Sir John about the School of Nursing which she proposed to start at St Thomas's Hospital. In discussing the provision of nurses for military hospitals he gave advice which probably would not meet with her approval (11 April 1859)—

> You propose to make nursing a respectable profession and to give the public the security of a certificate—must not all who gain certificates be left at liberty to pursue their profession in the manner and on the field that may be most advantageous to themselves, and must not the military hospitals go into the market and secure the best or at least good nurses by holding out superior inducements?

Miss Nightingale was not in favour of granting certificates to nurses and would probably answer in the negative, but her reply is not available. He helped her with the preliminary business arrangements and the drawing up of the agreement with St Thomas's for the Training School for Nurses, and he was one of the original members of the Council of the School. When the question of the agreement was being discussed he sent her a wise word of advice, dated 25 May 1859—

> The proposal, whenever it is made, ought to bear your signature on your own behalf, and that of Mr Herbert on behalf of the Council. If the heads that you may ultimately resolve to send are agreed to, then no doubt some explanation of details may be necessary, and when the whole is arranged it ought, I think, to be at once reduced to writing by men of business. Mere understandings almost always turn out to be misunderstandings.

Sir John McNeill had the utmost admiration for the character and attainments of Miss Nightingale. This was well shown in a letter he wrote to her on 19 November 1861—

> You have a strength and a power for good to which I never could pretend. It is a small matter to die a few days sooner than usual. It is a greater matter to work while it is day and so husband our powers as to make the most of the days that are given us. This you will do. Herbert and Clough and many more may fall around you but you are destined to a great work and you cannot die till it is substantially if not apparently done. You are leaving your impress on the age in which you live, and the print of your foot will be traced by generations yet unborn. Go on—to you the accident of mortality ought to be as the falling of the leaves in autumn.

He retired from his administrative post in 1868 and lived in active retirement until 1883, when he died at the ripe age of eighty-eight years.

6

The Army Medical College and its Professors

ONE OF THE FIRST THINGS which Miss Nightingale noted on her arrival at Scutari was the need for special training of the medical officers on active service. She observed that the young assistant surgeons had not been given any special instruction in the hygiene of camps or hospitals, and formed the opinion that they would benefit by a course in operative surgery. The sympathy which she felt for the young assistant surgeons in the Army may be judged by a memorandum in her handwriting written apparently when she was getting together her notes for the evidence she was to give before the Army Sanitary Commission. It ran as follows—

> Asst. Surgeons. Life of slavery. Like religious disabilities though more depressing because they do not feel it. Not ennobling like martyrdom.
>
> We fought for the freedom of national life of half the world leaving a whole class of fellow countrymen deprived of the most essential of all freedoms and of intellectual life, viz, scientific freedom. St Paul, had he been a M.O. never wd [*sic*] have been St Paul.

She even formed the project of starting a teaching centre at the seat of war. As early as three months after her arrival she wrote to Sidney Herbert a letter which must be accounted extraordinary as coming from a woman who had had no medical training herself. The letter is dated 22 February 1855. The relevant part is as follows—

> One thing which we much require might easily be done. This is the formation of a medical school at Scutari. We have lost the finest opportunity for advancing the cause of medicine and erecting it into a science which will probably ever be afforded. There is here no

operating room; post-mortem examinations are seldom made and then in the dead-house (the ablest staff-surgeon has told me that he considered that he had killed hundreds of men owing to the absence of these). No statistics are kept up as to between what ages most deaths occur, as to modes of treatment, appearances of the body after death, and all the innumerable and most important points which contribute to make therapeutics a means of saving human life, and not, as here, a formal duty. Our registration is so lamentably defective that often the only record kept is 'a man died on such a day.'

She not only saw the need but suggested the remedy.

There is a kiosk on the esplanade before the Barrack Hospital rejected by the quartermaster for his stores, which I have asked for and obtained as a school of medicine. It is not used now for any purpose. £300 or £400 (which I would willingly give) would put it in a state of repair. The young surgeons here are first rate anatomists, as good I dare say as any in London, but miserable pathologists. Morbid anatomy is almost unknown and the science of healing unpractised. At the request and according to the plan of the First Class Surgeons I gave them some expensive operating and dissecting tables, and I learn from them that they have pulled off the legs and burnt them as firewood.

The kiosk is not overlooked and is in every way calculated for the purpose I have named. The medical teaching duties could not be carried on efficiently with a less staff than two lecturers on physiology and pathology and one lecturer on anatomy who will be employed in preparing the subject for demonstration and performing of operations for the information of the juniors. If they could thus be interested in their profession (let alone in humanity) much vice would be checked, besides saving in future many hundreds of lives.

The supreme confidence with which these suggestions were made by one without any medical training and without any previous consultation with the principal medical officer, almost takes one's breath away. It is possible that the last sentence contains the chief clue to her strange suggestion. Nevertheless, though the scheme was impracticable and came to nothing at the time, it was noteworthy as showing Miss Nightingale's practical interest in the special training of army doctors, and as the original idea from which at a later date arose the establishment of the Royal Army Medical College.

The project of an Army Medical School was continuously in Miss Nightingale's mind during all the negotiations for the setting up of Royal Commission for investigating the sanitary state of the Army. In her first interview with Lord Panmure (October 1856) he had favourably received her suggestion that one of the objects of the Commission should be the establishment of such a School, and in the following month he had agreed with her that Colonel Lefroy should be asked to draft an outline scheme.

In December 1856 Dr Sutherland suggested to her that it would not be necessary to found a full medical school, but merely to give special instruction on such subjects as camping, ambulances, field operations, wounds, zymotic diseases, pathological anatomy, case-taking, statistics, climatology and sanitary reporting. She thought this insufficient and considered that Dr Sutherland's list was very vague and laid too much emphasis on field operations. As to the period of study necessary, she commented: ''Tis not so much teaching as practical training [which was needed] and therefore I say two years.'

Late in December 1856 Colonel Lefroy sent her the draft of the projected constitution of the School for her comments and criticisms.

On every section of the draft she made pungent criticisms and constructive suggestions.

In the first place she commented that in the whole draft insufficient notice had been taken of the previous training, scientific and practical, which the officer had undergone. She thought that a record of this should always be available, for in her opinion there was not enough practical work undertaken by the students, and she added—

> Our civil [medical] schools would not admit that they were deficient in practical instruction, but it may be shown that 5 per cent only can possibly enjoy the opportunity.

In the draft Colonel Lefroy suggested that the School should be situated near London so that it could be near the best medical talent and have ready access to the museums, lecture-rooms, and libraries of the great hospitals. On this point Miss Nightingale made the acute remark that as regards the use of the London medical libraries, 'these can only be obtained by the introduction of private friends owing to the constitution of these libraries. The libraries of the Medico-Chirurgical Society, and of the College of Surgeons are close boroughs by their constitutions.' As stated above, she also recommended a course of two years as against the one year suggested by Lefroy.

In the draft it was recommended that some of the teachers in the School should be in the Army, but others might be civilian physicians with large practices. Miss Nightingale commented: 'not a man in first-rate practice; he may be very incompetent to teach. A man with an eminent practice rarely indeed becomes an eminent teacher.' She was of opinion that good men might be found to do the teaching at £300 to £500 per annum, and made an additional practical suggestion that it might be wise to open a dispensary for poor patients wherein the students might obtain practice in clinical medicine. She thought it better to term the teachers 'tutors' rather than 'professors', and laid it down that they should be made to retire at the age of fifty-five years. She advised that the teachers should be fixtures, for 'the whole apparatus of a teaching man is quite a fixture if he takes to it. Teachers should therefore not be Army medical officers sent to stations or engaged in other duties.'

Lefroy had made the suggestion that some charge might be made to some of the students, 'making it in fact to a small extent an open medical school.' Concerning this, Miss Nightingale made the shrewd comment—

> Pupils should rather receive pay than give fees. It puts them in a more responsible position and they have already paid a large sum in their medical education—from £400 to £600. Eighty pounds per annum pay should be sufficient.

With regard to making the School open, she added—

> This would bring an opposition from all other medical schools. It should be merely a school of probationers and the pupils should be called not students but probationers.

It was proposed to choose candidates by competitive examination and to post successful candidates in the first place to a regiment for one year to 'break them in,' and then to send them to the Army Medical School for their special training. After that they would be again examined, and posted according to the results of this final test. Miss Nightingale asked indignantly—

'Breaking in?' what do the details of breaking in consist of? The more there are of medical men, the less of officers and mess-table men, the better. Breaking in better done in a hospital, if a military one. Go to school before you go to duty. Some may not be fitted for regimental duty at all, or even to enter the Army. Some may be fitted for other medical posts in the Army.

The final paragraph of the draft constitution dealt with its control, and the wording was as follows: 'The Institute should be under the Director-General of the Army Medical Department and a Board of Visitors, partly civilian; the Director-General of Military Education to be a member of it. Its correspondence with the Secretary of State should be through the Director-General of Military Education.' On this suggestion Miss Nightingale poured severe criticism. She wrote—

School should be independent. No Director-General nor any one man can know the requirements of the different teachers. We have committed a primary mistake in confounding the scientific and administrative functions in one man—the Director-General of the Army Medical Department—the consequence of which is that the former have gone to the bottom.

This forward-looking woman added a postscript of great significance which shows that she was at least fifty years ahead of her time in the matter of post-graduate education—

A most important part of this school would be to give medical officers from the Colonies, to whom periodical leave of absence should be granted specially for the purpose, an opportunity of renewing their knowledge and practice and bringing it up to the level which civil medical science raises higher every year.

The outline of the scheme for the Medical School was completed long before the Commission met, and, as is well known, one of the four sub-Commissions set up was given the business of implementing the scheme which had been outlined. But there were delays, some unavoidable, some due to the supineness or the deliberate lack of co-operation of the Army Medical Department. Miss Nightingale often used to repeat the words 'No report is self-executive,' and she prompted Mr Herbert to see that no unnecessary delays occurred. The War Office objected to any of the teaching posts being given to civilians and delayed the opening of the School till 1860. The nomination of the professors (for that term was ultimately applied to them) had been made by Miss Nightingale in 1857, but this was not definitely confirmed till 1859. Mr Thomas Longmore was made professor of surgery, Dr E. A. Parkes professor of hygiene, and Dr Aitken professor of pathology. A start had been made. It was well recognized at the time that the foundation of the School was the work of Miss Nightingale. In an address given at Fort Pitt in 1860 Professor Longmore stated—

> For originating this School we have to thank Miss Nightingale, who, had her long and persevering efforts effected no other improvements in the Army, would have conferred by this alone an inestimable boon upon the British soldier.

THE DOCTORS WHO WERE THE FIRST PROFESSORS AT THE ARMY MEDICAL COLLEGE

DR E. A. PARKES

Of the professors originally appointed to the College, one at least was an unqualified success—Dr E. A. Parkes, whom Miss Nightingale had come to know in the Crimean War. Parkes had had a distinguished career at University College Hospital Medical School and at the time when he went out to the seat of war (1855) was professor of clinical medicine at University College Hospital. He was asked by the Government to choose a suitable site and to set up a civil hospital which should relieve the pressure on the Military hospitals at Scutari. He selected Renkioi, where he superintended the hospital for a year.

Parkes was a man of high character and attainments. He was a

5. Sir J. McNeill (1797–1883)

(From 'The Illustrated London News', 1883)

6. Sir William Aitken (1825–92), first Professor of Pathology at the Army
Medical School, 1859–92

(From a photograph by A. J. Melhuish in the 'Prov. med. J.', Leicester, 1889)

Fellow of the Royal Society and had an international reputation in the field of hygiene. His writings and his research work brought reputation to the School and his high character inspired the students, while his wise administration and advice greatly helped to establish the School. In 1860, when the School was just starting at Chatham, he sent Miss Nightingale a syllabus of the lectures to be given, and a little later reported progress to her—

> So far I think nothing could have gone on better . . . both Longmore and Aitken are most efficient teachers and both are very popular.

Three months later he wrote: 'I wish we could hope . . . to have the pleasure of seeing you at Chatham and showing you our work, which is your work'; and in another letter: 'I do not like to remain longer without giving you some account of our school, the joint work of yourself and Lord Herbert.'

We have explained earlier that Miss Nightingale did not believe in contagion, nor in the view that cholera was due to the agency of a micro-organism which could be conveyed by water. These opinions she held most strongly and did not readily brook opposition to her views. Even Dr Parkes had to be diplomatic when his convictions caused him to hold different views from hers. In December 1861, for example, he wrote to her—

> I have always very strongly insisted on the portability of cholera. After reading your letter I felt a little anxious to explain my opinion on the mode of spread of cholera and on contagions generally . . . the evidence of the last 12 years has brought out some additional facts, and especially the *occasional* spread of the disease by the agency of water.

Mutual trust and friendship between them continued until, in 1876, Dr Parkes died of generalized tuberculosis. One of the last letters he wrote was to Miss Nightingale. The letter was dated 9 March 1876, and he died on 15 March. It is a moving tribute to Miss Nightingale and a remarkable testimony to the character of the writer.

MY DEAR MISS NIGHTINGALE

Your letter reached me on what must be, I believe, my deathbed. Perhaps before you receive this, I shall be summoned to my account.

6

For what you say, I thank you. About two months hence the S.P.C.K. will publish a little book on 'the personal care of health.' A copy will be sent to you. I had small space, only 26 pages, but I put in as much sanitary information as I could of a very simple kind. I hope it may be a little useful to you. It is addressed entirely to the poor. And now thank you and bless you for all the support you have always given me.

E. A. PARKES.

After his death Miss Nightingale wrote a tribute to his memory which was contained in a letter to Dr Acland (17 March 1876)—

MY DEAR SIR,

I have to thank you for your most valuable pamphlet on engineering and public health which I do most heartily.

The death of our dear friend Dr Parkes fills me with grief and also with anxiety for the future of the Army Medical School at Netley. He was a man of most rare modesty: of singular gifts. His influence on the School—there was not a man who did not leave it the better for having been under him—is irreplaceable. But the knowledge and instruction he has diffused from the School as a centre has extended and will extend wherever the English language is spoken, and beyond. To me his is almost the last pledge of those times with Sidney Herbert (who founded the School). He was the main spring of that watch. But I will not take up your time with enumerating Dr Parkes' powers and gifts, which you can appreciate better than I, ...

She goes on to express her fears for the future of the School, and then returns to describe the last days of Dr Parkes—

Dr Parkes died like a true Christian hero 'at the post' and the simplicity of one. I think I have never known such disinterestedness, such self-abnegation, such unnecessary and wise exertion for others, such forgetfulness of self. His death was like a resurrection. When he was dying he dictated letters—or gave messages to everybody—all about what ought to be done *for the School*, for the spread of hygienic knowledge, for other useful and Army purposes, none for himself. He actually wrote letters about our soldiers' valise equipment, about our soldiers' health, efficiency and comfort, and many other things pertaining to his various offices, prepared papers etc (one which will be published two months hence) till I think March 5th when he could no longer hold a pen. ... On March 15 he died perfectly clear in mind and leaving messages (by his friend Professor Longmore) as long as he could speak. It was truly the death of a hero. Let us, as he

went to the sacrifice of himself (he was only 56) with joy and praise
—as the heroes of old—so part with him. But let us try to save what
he would have saved.

Miss Nightingale knew well enough how to meet the threatened
disestablishment of the Medical School, just as in 1869 she had
prevailed on Mr Cardwell not to diminish its establishment. At
this time (1876) Mr Gathorne Hardy was War Secretary. For his
benefit she drew up the case for the maintenance of the School and,
to make quite sure that the Minister should himself hear the
appeal, she deputed her brother-in-law, Sir Harry Verney, to take
the memorandum to Mr Hardy, to solicit an interview and to
read it aloud to him. This unprecedented method of approach
might have prejudiced some persons against the petition, but in
this instance Mr Hardy listened intently but made no immediate
decision. Three weeks later he returned the papers to Sir Harry
with the welcome news that the School should continue as before.
Miss Nightingale had achieved another triumph.

MR THOMAS LONGMORE

The Professor of Surgery

Thomas Longmore was the first appointed professor of surgery at
the Army Medical School. He had served as medical officer in the
Light Brigade outside Sebastopol, with Dr Thomas Alexander as
his superior officer. He had been one of the few who had ventured
openly to complain of the bad conditions under which the troops
were serving and of the poor equipment provided for the Medical Service. In October 1854 he sent home a long letter, which
appeared in the *Daily News* on 8 November, in which he plainly
described the awful conditions around Sebastopol. Miss Nightingale nominated him on the recommendation of Dr Alexander,
when the latter was Director-General. Years passed before she
actually saw Longmore. In August 1864, when he specially wished
to interview her about some matter, she made special arrangements
for him to go to Hampstead (where she was then staying), and she

added the words: 'I should be sorry to go out of this world without seeing the friend of my dear friend Mr Alexander.' She allotted
fifteen minutes for the interview.

Soon after his appointment Miss Nightingale had some correspondence with Longmore about a Soldiers' Home which it was
proposed to establish at Chatham. This was to be a voluntary effort
with some Government assistance; the purpose was to provide a
place of recreation for the soldiers, somewhat similar to that
which she had provided for the troops at Scutari. The purpose
was clearly put by Miss Nightingale—

> We are anxious to extend, especially to Aldershot, where the abomi-
> nations which go on just outside the lines are such as are rarely seen
> in civilized life, the benefits of a place where the men can have
> refreshment, rest, amusement, which now they can only seek at the
> canteen or the public house when out of barracks.

Longmore was appointed as a representative to the International
Congress at Geneva, where the question of a voluntary international system of nursing and purveying was to be discussed. He
consulted Miss Nightingale about it, and she wrote—

> I need hardly say that I think its views most absurd, just such as
> would originate in a little state like Geneva, which never can see war.
> They think to remove responsibility from Governments.

Longmore sent her Dunant's pamphlet advocating the neutrality
of the medical services and the formation of what was to become
the Red Cross organization; this was to be known as the Geneva
Convention. Miss Nightingale had little use for it—

> I agree with you it will be quite harmless for our Government to sign
> the Convention as it now stands. It amounts to nothing more than a
> declaration that humanity to the wounded is a good thing. It is like
> an opera chorus, and if the principal European characters sing—
> 'We never will be cruel more,' I am sure if England likes to sing too
> 'I never will be cruel more,' I see no objection. But it is like vows.
> People who keep a vow would do the same without the vow. And
> if people will not do it without the vow, they will not do it *with*.
> England and France will not be more humane to the enemy's
> wounded for having signed the Convention, and the Convention will

not keep semi-barbarous nations like Russia from being inhuman. Besides which, though I do not reckon myself an inhuman person, I can conceive circumstances of 'force majeure' in war when the more people are killed the better.

After Mr Longmore had acted as professor for five years, he wrote to Miss Nightingale saying that he felt compelled to resign because by taking the appointment he had sacrificed stepping up the ordinary ladder of promotion, and consequently had lost the accompanying increase of pay. At once Miss Nightingale made representations in the proper quarter and was able to obtain an increase in remuneration sufficient to make it worth while for him to continue in the professoriate. In one of her letters to Longmore she told him that 'your loss would be irreplaceable.'

Longmore's correspondence with Miss Nightingale continued until 1882. One of the last letters he wrote to her concerned the training of nurses at Netley, where a special course of instruction was given for 'The National Aid Society of Nursing Sisters,' followed by an examination. Miss Nightingale wrote asking for a copy of the questions set. We know that she was not in favour of granting certificates on the strength of a written examination, but we do not know what were her comments on the papers.

Mr Longmore was knighted in 1887. He died in 1895. He wrote a standard work on *Gunshot Wounds* (1st ed., 1877; 2nd ed., 1895) and an excellent *Life of Richard Wiseman*.

SIR WILLIAM AITKEN (1825–1892)

Dr William Aitken was the first professor of pathology in the Army Medical School. The son of a doctor in practice at Dundee, he was born in 1825, and studied medicine in Edinburgh, where he took his M.D. in 1848. He thereupon was appointed pathologist to the Royal Infirmary, Glasgow. In 1855 he was sent out to the Crimea as assistant to Dr S. D. Lyons, who was commissioned to investigate the nature of the diseases from which the troops were suffering so severely. Miss Nightingale must have met Dr Aitken at Scutari, and it is indeed likely that she may have acquired her interest in morbid anatomy by reason of meeting him there. Otherwise it would have been strange for her to suggest the giving of lectures on that subject to the young officers at Scutari.

In 1860 Aitken was appointed professor of pathology at Fort Pitt, Chatham, where the Medical School was first placed. Initially he was merely nominated Curator of the Museum, but Sidney Herbert (and probably Miss Nightingale also) thought the post should be that of a professor, and thus it was arranged. Aitken had an uphill task to found a pathological museum, to fit up a pathological laboratory, and to teach pathology to the students. Many delays and hindrances occurred, and he sent many long and complaining letters to Miss Nightingale, appealing to her to use her influence to hasten matters towards completion. She was patient with his continual requests and usually managed to placate him. That there was reason for his complaints can be seen from the letter which Miss Nightingale wrote to Captain Galton on 3 September 1860—

MY DEAR CAPTAIN GALTON

On Saturday I had a letter from the professors of the Army Medical School—quite desperate. The authority for the instrument money had not yet come. Ten of the students had arrived. They stared at the bare walls and the absence of all arrangements for their work (in the new buildings) and concluded 'the school was a hoax.' Most unfortunate it is for the first impressions may have a serious effect upon the future of the School, and if one of these young men were to write to the *Lancet* it would 'damage' the School most completely. . . . It is really too much. I wish the War Office were at Timbuctoo. I am sure we should do much better without it. Although this School is but a small matter it is just a type and a climax of the working of the whole thing and I am very glad it has all happened. Because it is so. I shall just write to Mr Herbert and tell him of it.

Professor Aitken had a great opinion of her powers of observation, and on one occasion wrote to her asking if she had kept records of the temperature at Scutari in the winter months; he finished the request with the words:'unless I get the information from you I am not likely to get it at all.' On one occasion she wished to get notices put in some Glasgow papers and asked him if he would help in the matter. Aitken wrote back saying: 'I shall never be so busy but that I will always find time to do anything for you.'

He even gave her advice about the training of nurses when she was about to start the School at St Thomas's. His comments have a bearing even on the nursing of today—

> I would like to see the sphere of their education, however, more extended. If they are educated solely at one hospital they are sure to become bigots in all the ways of that hospital, and therefore besides the education at St Thomas's it were well for them to see the practice also of some small special hospitals.

At the end of the first year of the Army Medical School's existence there occurred a storm in a teacup, owing to a difference between the students and staff on the one hand and the management on the other. It was about the examination of the students before they were posted. Miss Nightingale was in favour of competitive examination for posting. One of the great objections which she had to the old system was the power of promotion and appointment entrusted to the Director-General, which enabled him (if he were so minded) to benefit those whom he liked rather than those who best merited promotion. In the initial regulations of the School it was recommended that there should be a competitive examination at the end of the School course, and that posting should be made according to the result of that examination. Now candidates for the Army Medical Service had to undergo a competitive examination in London before they could obtain entry to the Service; the results of that examination were made public, and it had been customary for them to form the basis of posting later. Apparently the first batch of students to enter the new college were not told, or at least did not understand, that there was to be a second competitive examination, held at the end of the course, which would be used for posting purposes. Consequently, when they were so informed they thought it unfair, and the professors sympathized with them.

The suggestion was made that a second examination might still be held but that it should not be competitive and should not form the basis for posting, which should be in accordance with the order of merit at the entrance examination. The Director-General (Gibson) visited the School and approved this suggestion, but said that he might take into consideration (privately) the results of the term examination. This was approved by the professors. Then next day, to their chagrin, the Director-General came down again, told them that Mr Herbert would not consent to that arrangement, and informed the student candidates that they would have to undergo a second competitive examination. This angered the professors, and annoyed the students many of whom had not taken great trouble to prepare for the end-of-term examination. Gibson put the blame on Herbert, but there can be little doubt that the final decision must have rested with Miss Nightingale. The following letter of complaint from Aitken must therefore have been an unpleasant surprise to her. It was dated 26 February 1861.

> I meant to have written to you ere now to tell you that the last act of our first session was completed on Thursday last; but I have waited to cool down a bit, fearing to write lest I might say something that were better left unsaid. The truth is that we all think that affairs have ended—not well as regards our relations with Dr Gibson on the one hand, and with the candidates on the other. As Dr Parkes writes me on the subject I will rather use his mild expressions (which are strong for his amiable nature) than write what I would say myself. He says 'the proceedings of the Director-General are remarkable and it is difficult to know what altered his policy in 24 hours.' But the minutes of the last meeting of the Senate (Wed. 20th) may bring on some little explanation from Gibson, which would not be a bad thing, as he has by his vacillation put the professors in a very awkward dilemma.
>
> You recollect, no doubt, my calling your attention to his policy of holding a second competitive examination with the candidates here. We were unanimous as to its being unfair to the men—and although Lord Herbert's first reply was opposed to our views and supported that of the Director-General yet his second letter withdrawing his first, appeared to be so distinct, etc., etc.

There was much more in the same strain, which made it clear that neither professors nor students would stand for a last-minute decision to impose upon them a decisive competitive examination, of which they had had no clear notification. The misunderstanding appears to have arisen because Lord Herbert had given instructions without prior consultation with Miss Nightingale. However, when she saw how serious was the opposition at the College she soon had the instructions altered, for on 2 March Dr Aitken wrote to her a grateful letter: 'Kind thanks once again for placing our train upon the proper line. We were shunted off so suddenly that we were all taken by surprise.' Dr Aitken was a successful teacher and writer. He published a text-book of medicine which was very popular and went through many editions. He was elected Fellow of the Royal Society, and in 1887, the Jubilee year, he was knighted. He remained in his post as professor until 1892. He then retired, and died within three months of his retirement.

7

The Directors-General
of the
Army Medical Department

SIR ANDREW SMITH (1797–1872)

Director-General 1853–1858

WHEN THE CRIMEAN WAR broke out, Dr Andrew Smith was Director-General of the Army Medical Department. He had had a distinguished career in the Army, which he had entered as 'hospital mate' in 1815. He had seen service for many years in South Africa, and it is stated that it was largely due to his advice that Natal became a colony of the British Crown. He was well known as an anthropologist and zoologist. War on the scale of the Crimea was outside his experience, and, moreover, he was provided with an absurdly small staff with which to carry out the many official duties assigned to him. His difficulties were increased by the fact that there were as many as five authorities which had to be consulted in connection with any hospital matter, and his personality was not strong enough to take the lead.

Miss Nightingale first met Dr Smith in October 1854 when she needed to get letters of authorization from him to enable her to go to the Crimea. These he readily granted, even before Sidney Herbert had given her authority to take sole control of the nurses who were going to Scutari. Much of the muddle which ensued in the first year of the campaign was not directly due to the Director-General but to a variety of unfortunate occurrences, many of which were not his fault. Dr Smith was at a great disadvantage in that he was far distant from the seat of war and therefore could not realize the exact position of affairs, and because he was dependent upon others for the carrying out of orders. Miss Nightingale had the supreme advantage of reporting directly to Sidney Herbert, over the head of Dr Smith. He, on his side, was dependent for his information upon reports from the principal medical officer and from other officers, and he could hardly have been pleased that confidential reports were being transmitted to the Minister through this unusual channel and without his knowledge of their contents.

When Miss Nightingale returned to England in 1856, burning with indignation and filled with zeal to put right the many sanitary and administrative wrongs she had seen, she did not put her case to the Director-General, but succeeded in her mission by obtaining the sympathy of Queen Victoria, and by a personal interview with Lord Panmure, the Minister of War. It was with Lord Panmure that she discussed who should be the members of the Sanitary Commission, and the Royal Warrant for that Commission was not shown to Sir Andrew until the Queen's signature had been appended to the document. This was purposely done to avoid objections from the Director-General.

It would have been surprising if there had been much goodwill between the two. Miss Nightingale was certainly scornful of Sir Andrew. When the latter was questioned by the Commission as to the method of promotion in the Army Medical Service, he explained the procedure current at that date, and concerning this, Miss Nightingale's comments were as follows—

> Did not A Smith's evidence yesterday amount to this? I act upon no rule. I have neither selection nor seniority. I erect myself into a judge of what is best for the interests of the service. I have under me gentlemen, educated men who are like beggars without any knowledge of what tomorrow's prospects are. They have no rule to depend upon but my judgement of what is best for the service. This is the system of Army Medical Government and I consider it a perfect one, perfectly administered.

At the Roebuck inquiry it was with some difficulty that Dr Smith was induced to give a grudging admission that the nurses who went out to the Crimea had done useful work.

As related in another chapter, Miss Nightingale, with great skill and astuteness, persuaded Lord Panmure to put on the Commission enough members who sympathized with her views to make sure that her recommendations would prevail. Sir Andrew Smith was a member, but he could easily be outvoted. At first he was opposed to the setting up of the Commission since he thought it would do more harm than good. It is quite likely that the way in which Miss Nightingale kept her own personality out of sight and worked almost entirely through her willing agents— Lord Herbert, Dr T. Alexander, Sir James Clark, Mr Augustus Stafford, and Sir J. Ranald Martin—contributed to the illusion that the members of the Commission were coming to completely independent judgements. Miss Nightingale did not herself give evidence before the Commission but sent a long written series of answers to a questionnaire. The written report of the Commission was in fact entirely the work of Miss Nightingale, assisted by Dr Sutherland. During the progress of the inquiry Sir Andrew became somewhat more sympathetic to the aims of the Commission and in due course he signed the report. He retired from the post of Director-General on 22 June 1858. Miss Nightingale was not sorry for this, for she thought he had held up the fulfilment of some of the recommendations of the Commission, and that it was essential that the next person who should fill the position should be sympathetic with measures of reform. As related elsewhere, she feared that Sir John Hall might be nominated to the vacancy, and by pressure in the right quarter she made sure that this would not happen. She induced Sidney Herbert to interview General Peel and to obtain the nomination of General Alexander for the post.

DR THOMAS ALEXANDER

Director-General 1858–1860

General Thomas Alexander served in the Crimea with distinction, and it was known that he had been very critical of the medical administration in that campaign. Dr Sutherland had strongly urged

Miss Nightingale to make every effort to get Alexander nominated for the Sanitary Commission, even though it meant bringing him back from Canada. This was in due course done. As we have seen, it was directly due to her efforts that Alexander was appointed Director-General on the retirement of Sir Andrew Smith. Sidney Herbert was pleased at this. He wrote to her (on 16 September 1858) saying how glad he was to have her account of Alexander, and continuing: 'Everything in future must depend on him. You cannot maintain a commission sitting permanently *in terrorem* over the Director-General, and Alexander seems able and willing to be his own commission.' Nevertheless, Miss Nightingale not only regarded him as her nominee but appeared to expect him to consult her on every matter of importance. He got to work quickly, and as early as 1 October 1858 a Royal Warrant was issued for improved pay and relative rank of army medical officers; at the same time definite rules for promotion were laid down, higher qualifications for entry to the Service were insisted upon, and future entries to the Service were to be by competitive examination. All these changes were in accord with the recommendations of the Commission and in keeping with Miss Nightingale's views.

But Alexander soon earned her displeasure. Sir John McNeill had suggested that there should be an advisory medical board for the Army Medical Service. Alexander had the temerity to nominate two members of this board on his own initiative, without consulting either Lord Herbert or Miss Nightingale. This brought down on his head the wrath of that lady, who, in a letter dated 24 March 1859, wrote as follows to Sir John—

> I want the more to put you in possession of the facts regarding the Army Medical Board (of which you were the original inventor and which Alexander has cruelly mangled)—Alexander goes and surreptitiously (without saying a word to Mr Herbert) recommends two of his creatures to General Peel who are forthwith appointed so that the Board is nothing now but one more of the hugger-mugger boards of Andrew Smith's plus Balfour. I hear that Alexander is heartily ashamed of himself. But it is too late now. He has made himself another example of the regular official who does not like able or independent men about him 'et surtout point de zèle.' I am

not at all of your friend Socrates' opinion that it is better to perish by other people's folly. I think nothing is so provoking. If Lord Panmure had done this thing now I should not have minded.

It is clear that she was provoked because she had not been allowed a say in the matter. If we are to believe a writer in the *Naval and Miltary Gazette* for 11 February 1860, Mr Alexander was himself greatly discouraged by the way events had developed. He was severely criticized by both sides. The article in the *Gazette* stated—

> Of Mr Sidney Herbert's earnest desire to promote the best interests of the Medical Officers, considering them identical with those of the soldier and the public, no doubt is entertained, but unfortunately he has fallen into the hands of a clique of dilettanti, who have no practical knowledge to guide them, and who had led him to ignore the Director-General so completely that Mr Alexander's determination to resign his appointment was no secret.

There can be little doubt as to the significance of the word 'clique' in this passage, and the rumour that Alexander was about to resign may have had some foundation.

It was fortunate for the reformers that Alexander was in office sufficiently long to bring about many of the needed reforms, for any further development along the same lines was cut short by his early death in January 1860. His short period of office had meant a great deal to the Medical Service.

DR (afterwards Sir) JAMES BROWN GIBSON
Director-General 1860–1867

After the death of Alexander, Miss Nightingale lost touch with the Army Medical Department, though, as we have already seen, she still was referred to in case of difficulties. There is no record of any correspondence between Dr James Brown Gibson and herself, but we do know that she did not approve of him. In a letter dated 13 August 1864, written to Sir James Clark, she commented—

> Gibson was born to be our ruin. He is the mere tool of the Commander in Chief. The Horse Guards are the real Army Doctor

Managers. . . . I am intriguing now to get Muir back as Gibson's successor. . . . Gibson has done his worst to do away with examinations and get back nomination.

In this intrigue she was unsuccessful. Gibson went out of office in March 1867 and was succeeded by Dr (afterwards Sir) Thomas Galbraith Logan, who remained in office till 1874. Only then did Dr Muir (afterwards Sir William Muir) become Director-General. During his tenure of office there was a possibility of war against Russia. Sir William visited Miss Nightingale at her residence in South Street with a view to arranging for suitable nurses to be sent out. Fortunately the war scare passed off safely.

SIR THOMAS CRAWFORD

Director-General 1882-1889

Muir was succeeded in 1882 by Sir Thomas Crawford. In him Miss Nightingale found a man who was readily accessible, and open to receive suggestions, and even ready to ask for advice. He arranged for the sending out to Egypt of nurses whom she had recommended, and he took the trouble to let her know of their movements.

In 1883 he had a conversation with her to discuss the question of the extension of female nursing in the military hospitals. The following day she sent him a full memorandum on the subject in which she emphasized two main points which should be attended to if the proposed extension were to be carried out.

First, there should be thorough training both as to work and discipline, and secondly, there would have to be efficient supervision. Without these essentials it would be better not to have female nurses at all. In her opinion there ought never to be less than three nurses together at any post, and they should not be stationed at a hospital of less than 100 beds. She insisted that the orderlies ought also to be trained. 'If the trained woman is indispensable the trained man is so too. Neither must cause us to dispense with the other or both will come to grief.' She was of the opinion that a military hospital was not a suitable field in which to train probationers. 'All that can be learned at a military hospital is military practice and ward management, and what a soldier is.' She also gave an interesting list of questions which should be asked of those who wished to enter as military nurses. Four months later she forwarded to the Director-General a draft set of regulations for the proposed military nursing service.

Early in 1885 nurses had to be sent out to Egypt. At Miss Nightingale's request a small number went out under the charge of Miss Rachel Williams. Sir Thomas wrote (on 21 February 1885): 'There are only three nursing sisters going with Miss Williams. I am greatly gratified to know these arrangements have your concurrence.'

Later Miss Nightingale received letters from Miss Williams containing complaints, and she wrote to Sir Thomas asking details about the nurses' movements. On one occasion she was so peremptory as to send a messenger who was to await a reply from the Director General. He may have become a little impatient himself, for he wrote to her on 18 May—

> I suppose the proposed withdrawal of the troops has disarranged our plans for Miss Williams and her staff. Please leave the matter in my hands for the present. Miss Williams is, as you are aware, employed by us and consequently under the local authorities who will no doubt provide for her when they see their future more closely.

The very next day Sir Thomas telegraphed asking for the return of those nurses who could be spared, and Miss Williams soon returned to England.

In 1887 Sir Thomas gave Miss Nightingale assistance in another matter. The Commission of 1856–8 had set up a permanent Sanitary sub-Commission or Commission on which Dr Sutherland was the chief member. In 1887 Dr Sutherland wished to retire, as well he might in his eightieth year. There was some danger that the Commission might then lapse. Miss Nightingale exerted herself to have the Commission reconstituted, and discussed the matter with Sir Thomas. When Dr Sutherland retired in 1888 he was succeeded by Mr Marston, while Sir Douglas Galton remained on

7. William Farr (1807–83), the famous medical statistician, who spoke of Miss Nightingale as 'one of my aptest workmen'

(*From an engraving in the possession of the Royal Society of Medicine*)

8. John Croft (1833–1905), who for many years lectured to the nurses at the Nightingale Training School at St Thomas's Hospital

(From 'The Lancet', 1905)

and was joined by Mr J. W. Cunningham as the third member. Miss Nightingale and Sir Thomas drew up a revised constitution for the Commission.

As a final seal of her friendship for Sir Thomas, Miss Nightingale asked him to serve on the Council of the Nightingale Fund—an honour which she reserved for those for whom she had a great regard. Of him she said: 'We have not had such a man of unflagging energy since Alexander.' That was high praise. Sir Thomas Crawford died on 12 October 1895.

8

Dr William Farr
the Medical Statistician

MISS NIGHTINGALE, as a young woman, found mathematics easy to learn, and all her life she was interested in figures as well as facts. It was no wonder, therefore, that she set a great value upon statistics and, whenever possible, used them to force home a point or to carry conviction. It was no accident that one of her best friends was Dr William Farr, the virtual founder of medical statistics, whose acquaintance she made soon after her return from the Crimea. Dr (afterwards Sir) Ranald Martin had recommended Farr to her as one who would be a very suitable member of the proposed Commission to inquire into the sanitary state of the Army, and she did in fact put him down on her first list of possibles. Though finally his name did not appear among the members of the main Commission, Miss Nightingale frequently called upon him to give information and advice at all stages of the work of the Commission, and later he was made a member of the sub-Commission for Statistics. Early in 1857 she was interested in the mortality in hospitals and wrote to Farr as follows—

MY DEAR SIR,

I am not going to worry you. This is only to be a 'retainer.' I have received from the Registrar-General the mortality statistics of the London Hospitals which are very much the same as what I had been led to expect from the private returns I have. You would, however, derive great joy and satisfaction (as I should say if I were writing a Chadwickiad) for the one fact they point out is that the mortality increases as the number of patients. There are some differences between the hospitals which, however, can be explained by some taking in worse cases than others. 7·9 deaths in every 100 cases treated is the general rate in general hospitals, 9·38 in workhouses, 11·48 in special hospitals. The rest of my agreeable information I defer till I have the pleasure of seeing you again.

About the same time she must have asked him to help in connection with the statistics of health in the Army, for on 9 February 1857 he sent her the volumes of the proceedings of the Statistical Society dealing with hospital statistics, together with McCullough's work (a statistical account of the British Empire). On 14 February he followed up these with a promise to help.

It will always give me the greatest pleasure to render you any assistance I can in promoting the health of the Army. We shall ask your assistance in return in the attempts that are now being made to improve the health of the civil population.

He added his opinion about the part women could play in promoting sanitary measures—

It is in the house—the home—that sound principles will work most salutarily, and the effective agents must be the women of the country. I think that a small quiet society of ladies might suggest many valuable practical rules—and might contrive better ways than we know of making the rules work.

When Miss Nightingale was preparing her convincing proof of the bad sanitary state of the soldiers' barracks in this country, by showing that the death rate in them was much higher than among men of a similar age in the civilian population living under slum conditions, Dr Farr sent her encouragement and help. On 16 May 1857 he wrote—

I have read with much profit your admirable observations. It is like light shining in a dark place.

At the same time he showed her how she could make her points more clearly, and added—

You must, when you have completed your task, give some explanation for the sake of the ignorant reader. Nothing is more difficult to describe than machinery in motion, and when that machinery is living the description is not rendered easier.

When, later in the year, he was shown the diagrams she had drawn, and had read the accompanying description, his enthusiasm knew no bounds—

> This speech is the best that ever was written on diagrams or on the Army. I can only express my opinion briefly in 'Demosthenes himself with the facts before him could not have written, or thundered a better.' The details appear to be quite correct, but when I recover from the effect of the display of the great appalling subject, and have the diagrams before me, I will look into them again. It is however the perfection of writing with diagrams and tables before you, to render any reference to them by the reader unnecessary. This you have done.

Miss Nightingale returned the compliment three months later when on 5 February 1858 she wrote to him—

> I contemplated this morning with intense satisfaction the first fruits of your labours—the first publication of any return regarding the health of our army.

Miss Nightingale gave all her time to the projects she had in hand; her secluded life brooked no interruptions. Her medical colleagues had many things to attend to other than the particular projects which they had in common. It was perhaps natural that sometimes she should become impatient. The following letter (dated 1 March 1858) sufficiently explains itself—

> DEAR DR FARR,
>
> It is my misfortune to be a sandwich between two eminent men. Our 'Regulations' have hung fire and I have not been able to prepare a scheme of duties for the new 'Army Medical Council' because Dr Farr would not write the Statistical Reporting 'Regulations' until Dr Sutherland had written the Sanitary ones—and Dr Sutherland would not write the Sanitary Reporting 'Regulations' until Dr Farr had written the Statistical ones. Dr Sutherland however has the merit of having given in first and has dictated (or condescended to approve) the enclosed—and if Dr Farr would now issue his commands or Regulations for Statistical Reporting he would much advance the interests of his devoted and grateful admirer.

Miss Nightingale had definite ideas on hospital construction and wrote two papers on that subject for the Social Science Congress which was held at Liverpool in October 1858. Dr Holland, on her behalf, read the papers at the meeting, and Dr Farr reported to her that 'your papers were read to large audiences and were well received.' He added that 'the president was evidently struck by your attack on contagion and laughed heartily at the quarantine goose.'[1] Farr introduced the papers with a few explanatory words—

> Miss Nightingale directs our attention to the means we have of investigating the influence of hospitals on the patients. . . . These papers display very strikingly the practical character of Miss Nightingale's mind. She has visited hospitals. She has lived in hospitals. She has now submitted to the Section a series of plans which have been struck out by her sagacity.

It was in this year that Dr Farr asked her if she would like her name to go forward as a candidate for the membership of the Statistical Society. She consented and was duly elected a member.

In 1859 Miss Nightingale arranged that Dr Farr should be a member of the Indian Sanitary Commission; on 2 June she notified him that he had been gazetted as a member of the Commission on 31 May 1859. From this time forward for another fifteen years Dr Farr was in constant communication with her on every statistical subject of common interest and on many other subjects.

We have noted above that she was very interested in hospital statistics. Each big hospital kept its statistical report in its own way. There was no uniformity and no reliable method of comparison. Miss Nightingale (in 1859) tried to get the main hospitals in London to adopt a common form of registration of diseases, together with a uniform plan of publishing their results of treatment and mortality. Favourable replies were received from St Thomas's, University College Hospital, St Bartholomew's,

---

[1] The passage referred to ran as follows—And now, what does contagion mean? It implies the communication of disease from person to person by contact. It presupposes the existence of certain germs like the sporules of fungi, which can be bottled up and conveyed any distance attached to clothing, to merchandise, especially to woollen stuffs for which it is supposed to have a particular affection, and to feathers, which of all articles it especially loves—so much so that, according to quarantine laws, a live goose may be safely introduced from a plague country, but if it happens to be eaten on the voyage, its feathers cannot be admitted without danger to the entire community. There is no end to the absurdity connected with the doctrine.

St Mary's, and Guy's Hospitals, and for a time it looked as if some common ground might be found. The scheme, though a worthy one, ultimately came to nothing, probably because there was at that time no true scientific method of classifying diseases. Miss Nightingale had the idea that the ward sisters might help in the recording of diseases! The passage in which she mentioned this ran as follows—

> I do wish we could have composed some hospital books for the Statistics. Several superintendents of nurses have told me how glad they should be to make the 'Sisters' keep such returns. When I told Dr Sutherland he was all agog; and went off upon the 'rights' of man. Now I don't want this to interfere with the 'rights' of Registrars at all. They must do the official returning business if it is ever done, according to the system, of course. But I don't see why the poor women should not have the practice, merely for practice, by no means for official purposes, if it is good for them. Only we must compose hospital books for them (entries or ledger books).

We should gather from this suggestion that the nursing sisters of that time were not so fully occupied as the sisters of today.

At this point in her career nursing questions took a secondary place in Miss Nightingale's life. She was primarily interested in the sanitary problems of hospitals and of the Army. She put aside rather indefinitely the opportunity of reforming nursing which had been provided by the gift of the Nightingale Fund. It was the doctors who reminded her of the responsibilities in that direction. On 23 February 1858 Dr Farr wrote to her—

> I think more seriously than ever of the Institute for Nurses of whom . . . 25,465 were returned at the census for 1851. . . . and to make a few of them the disciples of the true doctrine of health would be a great national work.

He did not cease to remind her, for on 16 September of the same year he asked 'Have you thought further of the nurse foundation or school?' Early in 1859 he must have repeated his question and drawn from Miss Nightingale a query as to why he thought there was any need for hurry. He replied—

> Why is what we are to do to be done quickly? You are going to found a great and lasting institute. The sooner the acorn of this

mighty oak is in the soil the better; and for many years it will require your fostering care and genius to make it prosper. Good nurses can, I believe, be created by you out of English women, and if only two or three are completely formed they will multiply in a geometrical progression, 1, 2, 4, 8, but here as in the compound interest of money—to gain time is everything.

There were many other subjects of interest discussed between these two friends. From the following playful letter written by Dr Farr one might conclude that Miss Nightingale was very fond of tea.

Have you heard of the discovery of a new and somewhat startling reading of the sixth commandment which is likely to give rise to much controversy among the Rabbis learned in Hebrew MSS? As I cannot send you the Hebrew I send you the English translation. 'VI. Thou shalt not take tea.' Some Rabbis, among others Kinchi, contend that (too much) is by a common laconism omitted between the words 'Take' and 'Tea'. We must consider the question in all its bearings before our sanitary tablets are engraved finally.

Dr Farr valued the friendship and the correspondence between them, and when, late in 1859, she wrote (through Mrs Smith) in a desponding vein and told him that she thought she had not long to live, and requested him to destroy all the letters she had written to him, he wrote back—

I have always considered Miss Nightingale's letters confidential and I have this morning (with great regret) burnt all that I could find. Tell her that in looking through them I met with so much wit and wisdom that I feel I have been guilty of a sort of sacrilege for which she must ask the Gods to forgive me.

Three months later he may have regretted his action still more, for he wrote to her—

I do not ask how you are—as I always learn your life's estate from the activity I see going on around me. I am glad that you have launched your 'Great Eastern',[1] the medical school.

Dr Farr wrote for the *Lancet* and had ready access to its columns. Miss Nightingale made a convenience of this facility, as when

[1] The *Great Eastern*, the first large steamship to be built of iron, had been launched in 1858.

in 1860 she sent him a note with regard to something which Mr Herbert wanted—

> He would be very much obliged to you to write up his new Army Medical School in the *Lancet*. Because he expects a 'row' when the estimates come on (three weeks hence) and wishes to be able to quote from the civil medical papers.

Dr Farr replied next day—

> I have sent off the article to the *Lancet* with an additional sentence or two and have requested them to insert it.

From this reply we must conclude that Miss Nightingale had written an article on the Army Medical School, and sent it on to Farr, who merely added a few sentences before sending it on to the *Lancet*, whose readers might reasonably have concluded that the opinions therein expressed were quite independent of the sponsors of the school. No doubt the end justified the means.

After studying the statistics of the various hospitals in London Miss Nightingale became interested in the question of mortality after operations, which at that time was very great owing to the prevalence of hospital gangrene and other septic conditions. She asked Farr for his assistance in looking through the figures. He helped her considerably and sent her a memorandum on some 'table of amputations'. He told her, 'it is rough but will be intelligible to you—one of my aptest workmen.'

When the Congress of Statisticians was held in Berlin in 1863 Farr asked her whether she would contribute a paper. She replied that the only paper she had on hand was that on the mortality after surgical operations, which she forwarded for his inspection and opinion. He was pleased with it and in due course it was read before the Congress. In this paper Miss Nightingale pleaded for improved statistics of the results of operations. She had collected statistics of 482 fatal operations and had found that in 190 (40 per cent) the fatal result had been due to pyaemia, erysipelas and the like septic complications. She claimed that these diseases were notoriously 'connected with defective sanitary conditions in wards, or with conditions in patients so bad as to render doubtful the propriety of operating.' In some hospitals peritonitis was the chief cause of death, in others pyaemia, while in only a few hospitals was the number of deaths due to these causes very small. She drew attention to the need for more uniform statistics and suggested a suitable form which might be made use of in collecting the requisite data. It is well known that the publication of her views on this subject added fuel to the fiery question as to the cause of 'hospitalism'. Lawson Tait admired her character and agreed in the main with her views, which, until the publication of Lister's famous paper in the *Lancet* in 1867, were not easy to counter.

In 1856 Farr sent her an account of the latest results of the operations for ovariotomy performed by Spencer Wells. Her comments were characteristic—

> The figures are satisfactory but they would be more satisfactory if Mr Spencer Wells could take a small house in the country, high and dry, and operated there. However this operation is evidently entering the domain of operative surgery with a fair chance of good results.

This investigation led her to compare the mortality of different hospitals with the view of criticizing those which had a greater mortality—an invidious task. On 15 November 1862 she wrote to Farr reminding him that some time previously he had published a table of mortality of the various London hospitals, and adding a request—

> Could you give me such a table for such a number of years as would enable a general life-table of the London hospitals to be calculated. It would tell very much if we could show that each hospital had its own life-risk, and would add another argument to the case against these hospitals.

It will be noted that she was apparently not asking for information to ascertain the truth of a doubtful question, but to enable her to be provided with arguments which she could use to support her already definitely held convictions.

Sometimes Dr Farr tried to induce her to be less dogmatic and more open-minded on questions which were still unproven; but

she would not listen to him. He wrote her a long letter in which
he explained his views—

> Well, I admit all the evil that has been done in the name of 'contagion.'
> Yet I have looked into the question of contagion, not only in the case
> of small pox, measles, scarlatina, whooping cough, typhus, syphilis,
> erysipelas, but particularly in cholera. I believe that under *certain
> circumstances* a leaven is generated which under certain conditions
> will leaven the whole lump. But I hold that quarantine is a trumpery
> and mischievous impostor and cannot keep cholera out of a country ;
> neither can it keep any other zymotic disease out of a population
> prepared by unfavourable sanitary conditions to receive it. The
> contagionists and the anti-contagionists are I believe fanatics of the
> most desperate description on whom even our reason is thrown
> away. I therefore refuse to discuss the scholastic subtleties of the said
> sects and take my stand on this.

Her counter-arguments are interesting and throw light upon her
non-compromising character—

> I do not admit your definition of fanaticism, nor that truth can be
> fanatical. Either your contagionists are in the right and then they
> are not fanatical, or your non-contagionists are in the right, and they
> are not fanatical. Both cannot be fanatical any more than both can
> be in the right. Quarantine follows logically and inevitably on con-
> tagion, as sanitary measures on non-contagion. Farther than this I do
> not venture to argue with you because, as you say, I am not scientific.

Dr Farr had evidently made very little impression.

Miss Nightingale was a good propagandist. A paper read by her
before the National Association for Social Science does not appear
to have been published in the official transactions. This made her
indignant. She wrote to Farr—

> Are you not the greatest impostor that ever was? What did I wait
> for my paper from July till March for, except to have the names and
> opinions of all the wise men appended to it, which goes so far in this
> country?
>   yours sincerely altho' in extreme old age.

But Dr Farr knew how to placate her. In his reply a week later he
offered to have copies of the paper sent to the hospitals. She joyfully replied—

> I eagerly snatch at your offer to send copies to the principal hospitals
> —with a note signed by the secretaries of the Congress. Because you

see that is all that makes the paper likely to be practically followed, viz, the adhesion of the Congress.

Her enthusiasm for statistics was shown in one of the later letters to Farr. It was on the occasion of the death of Quetelet (1874).

> I cannot say how the death of our old friend touches me; the founder of the most important science in the whole world: for upon it depends the practical application of every other and of every art: the one science essential to all political and social administration, all education, and organization based on experience, for it only gives exact results of our experience.

Dr Farr died in 1883. When he retired in 1880 a subscription was raised for his benefit to which Miss Nightingale subscribed ten pounds. After his death she sent another hundred pounds to the Fund, which altogether amounted to only seventeen hundred pounds.

9

The Doctors at St Thomas's Hospital

AT THE TIME that Miss Nightingale started the Training School for
Nurses at St Thomas's Hospital the general standard of nursing was
not high, the 'sisters' in charge of wards were given no regular
training, and the ordinary nurses had the status of ward-maids or
scourers. By experience some of them became skilful and useful,
but many of them were of the Sairey Gamp type. We have pointed
out how Miss Nightingale was not in a hurry to found the school
and that several doctors thought fit to try and expedite the foundation of the school. It was founded in 1860 and was administered by a Council which was quite independent of the hospital,
though the nurses in training were provided for out of the Nightingale Fund. The Governors of the hospital gave permission for the
probationers in training to work in the wards. At the time that the
School was founded, St Thomas's Hospital was still situated
opposite Guy's Hospital near London Bridge.

St Thomas's Hospital had been chosen for the experiment, not
on account of the distinction or character of the medical staff—
though that was high—but largely because it had a capable matron,
Mrs Wardroper, who seemed to possess the moral and disciplinary
character which Miss Nightingale deemed necessary for the new
venture.

Not every member of the medical staff made the nurses welcome. The most antagonistic member was the senior surgeon,
Mr J. F. South, who had the old-fashioned ideas of nursing which
were current before the time of this attempt at reform. He bitterly
opposed the new scheme, for he believed that nurses needed little
training. In a pamphlet published in 1857, when first the idea of a
nurse-training school was being discussed, he gave his opinion

that the sisters or head nurses who were in charge of the wards at St Thomas's, 'for modesty and self-respect will bear comparison with a like number of women in any class of society.' His view of the ordinary nurse was expressed in the following words: 'the day-nurse or ward-maid performs for the ward the usual duties of a house-maid as to cleaning and bed-making.' He further enlarged on this statement—

> As regards the nurses or ward-maids, these, as I have said, are much in the position of housemaids and require little teaching beyond that of poultice-making, which is easily acquired, and the enforcement of cleanliness and attention to the patients' wants. They need not be of the class of persons required for sisters, not having such responsibilities.

It was not surprising therefore that he continued—

> as a general rule the nurses do not stay in the same hospital or the same ward more than a year or two, being like many household servants, fond of a change.

In this same pamphlet Mr South referred to another (anonymous) pamphlet which had been published in 1851 on the system of training at the Kaiserswerth Institution; Mr South probably knew that this pamphlet had been written by Miss Nightingale, for he speaks of the writer 'whoever he or she may be.' He denied emphatically the charges of drinking and immorality brought against English nurses by the writer. Most of Mr South's published remarks on the question seem to have been aimed at Miss Nightingale, though he only once mentioned her by name. In a letter to Mr Baggallay, the Treasurer of St Thomas's Hospital, he makes a complaint about the new nurses—

> I do not consider that any change to so-called lady nurses and to their control under external authority, although it may be that of Miss Nightingale, will be conducive to the patients' welfare or permit the medical and surgical duties of the hospital being carried on without frequent collisions, of which the military hospitals in the last war have presented numerous examples.

He added that he was about to communicate with his surgical colleagues on the subject with a view to a combined protest against the new 'Lady-Nurses', but he appears to have been the only active opponent of the scheme, and nothing of a concerted protest occurred.

In another part of this letter Mr South commented—

> I regret exceedingly that the surgeons have not been consulted in this matter—the intention of which, however carefully concealed, is to change entirely the whole nursing establishment of the house and to place it in the hands of persons who will never be content till *they* become the executive of the Hospitals, and as they have in the Military Hospitals been a constant source of annoyance to the Medical and Surgical Officers.

Mr South claimed that many others shared his views, and in this he was probably right, for in many hospitals in which the new nursing system was introduced, there ensued considerable trouble. These opponents would probably have sympathized with the unenterprising views he championed—

> So far as we, the hospitals, are concerned [he wrote] a training institution for our sisters and nurses is entirely unnecessary and superfluous. That this proposed hospital nurse-training scheme has not met with the approbation or support of the medical men is beyond all doubt. The very small number of medical men whose names appear in the enormous list of subscribers to the fund to enable Miss Nightingale to establish an institution for training nurses cannot pass unobserved. But the remarkable fact remains to be pointed out that of the ninety-four physicians, including principal, assistants, accoucheurs and consulting physicians, and of the seventy-nine principal and assistant surgeons of the seventeen hospitals of London, only three physicians and a surgeon from one, and one physician from a second hospital are found among the supporters of the scheme. This seems to me accounted for by their knowledge of the nursing establishments of their hospitals being as near as can what they should be, and perhaps also may be considered an indication of their disapproval of the observations made of the establishments with which they are connected, by individuals who had not knowledge of the subject on which they undertook to descant.

We fear that the reading of this tirade will not impress the modern reader with any high opinion of the perspicacity of the medical profession of that time. Mr South belonged to the old school of surgeons and was over sixty years of age when the nursing school began at St Thomas's. He was undoubtedly correct in saying that there were some excellent head-nurses at his hospital, yet in the main the indictment made by Miss Nightingale was certainly correct. Mr South's criticism made little impression, as may be judged by the remarks made in a letter written by Mr R. H. Goolden to Mrs Wardroper—

> It is only due to you after Mr South's pamphlet about Miss Nightingale's nurses that I should state to you that I consider their introduction a great advantage and blessing to the Hospital.
>
> The whole arrangement for the nursing since 1858 is most satisfactory and a great contrast to what it was before that time. . . . The advantage of training women for the special duties of nurses is so obvious to all persons, not only medical men, that I need hardly say that even some sacrifices should be made to do so—but when that training is an advantage instead of a sacrifice to a great hospital I consider it the duty of everyone connected with such an establishment to lend their aid.

Mr South retired in 1863, and the reform of nursing went on in spite of his angry protestations.

Of the nine members of the Council of the Nightingale Fund, four were doctors—Sir James Clark, Dr (afterwards Sir) William Bowman, Sir John McNeill, and Dr Bence Jones—but it is noteworthy that not one of them belonged to St Thomas's. The apothecary or resident medical officer at the hospital—Dr R. G. Whitfield —at first worked well in co-operation with the authorities of the School. He supervised the medical part of the nurses' education, and Miss Nightingale often consulted him on doubtful points. In 1859 she wrote to him to ask his opinion about Dr Bowman's project of founding a hospital for women's diseases which should be staffed by a woman doctor and nurses. She had in mind to ask Dr Blackwell, then the only registered woman doctor, to collaborate in the project. Dr Whitfield expressed the opinion (probably correct at that time) that a woman doctor would not be acceptable.

The most important collaboration between Miss Nightingale and Dr Whitfield was in connection with the moving and rebuilding of St Thomas's Hospital in the eighteen-seventies. When the South Eastern Railway wished to build London Bridge Station, they found it necessary to acquire part of the area then occupied by St Thomas's Hospital, and for some time there was a great and animated debate as to whether the hospital should be rebuilt on the truncated and restricted site, or whether it should be erected on a more convenient site some distance away. Several places were suggested, of which the Stangate site (the present position) was the most favoured. Dr Whitfield strongly supported moving the hospital to a new site. After full consideration Miss Nightingale also became an energetic advocate of the moving of the hospital.

The Prince Consort was a Governor of St Thomas's, and, on Dr Whitfield's suggestion, Miss Nightingale wrote to the Prince and put to him the arguments for the removal of the hospital. In the end, as everybody knows, the Stangate site was chosen and the present noble building was erected there.

Dr Whitfield, at the time that he took over the supervision of the medical part of the education of the probationers, was already comparatively senior, and, although he at first made some attempt to adopt the scheme which Miss Nightingale had outlined, he did not show the energy nor the keenness which was expected of him. It was part of the plan that the nurse-probationers should write short notes about the illnesses of the patients whom they were looking after, and Miss Nightingale asked Whitfield to formulate a few simple instructions which might help them in their task. His attempts were not successful, and he gradually seemed to become more critical of the whole scheme of training. He was bold enough to tell her: 'I do not approve of the combination of diary with case-taking.' A little later, in response to a request that he should insert some information about 'consumption' in the notes for the nurses, he commented: 'I shall have much pleasure in giving some special directions on consumption, . . . but as regards the introduction of points of nursing into the history of the case, and medical treatment, I think it would be objectionable.' This was in 1863.

In spite of their differences of opinion Miss Nightingale lent

him her support when he came into conflict with the authorities of
the hospital, and he continued to give her considerable help.

In 1866 he assisted in an inquiry into the relative mortality of
those nursed in hospital compared with those with similar diseases
nursed at home. In 1868 he gave her his considered advice as to the
nursing needs of a hospital in Sydney. His reports were always
full and clear. He wrote on one side of the paper only and left a
wide margin, 'thinking it more convenient for you to make
your observations.' He knew Miss Nightingale's habits.

There came a time, however, when Dr Whitfield had to give
up his connection with the School. In 1872 it was found necessary
to take over one of the rooms in the nurses' sick-bay to serve as a
bedroom for the newly installed superintendent of the School.
Unfortunately (or was it of set purpose?) Dr Whitfield was not
consulted about this, and when he found out he was angry and
sent an almost impertinent letter of complaint to Miss Nightingale.
It happened, however, that she had also been receiving private
and reliable information that he had been slack in his duties, and
was entirely neglecting any teaching of the probationers. He
had also quarrelled with Mr Croft, one of the surgeons, and
did not now enter the wards. Miss Nightingale therefore did
not reply to his letter. He thereupon sent her another note in
which he started by saying that he understood that representations had been made accusing him of supineness in his duties with
regard to the nurse-training, and excusing himself by saying that
his duties did not now take him into the hospital. He then filled
the remainder of a long letter with the most severe criticism of the
whole scheme of nurse-training. He thought too much was being
attempted, and added that for the nurses 'on Sunday there might
be a bible class—all other classes should be ignored.'

This was too much for Miss Nightingale. She did not send any
reply and declared she would never communicate with him again.
She wrote to Mr Bonham Carter asking him to interview Dr
Whitfield and ask him to resign from his connection with the
School. Mr Bonham Carter interviewed Whitfield, who immedi-
ately sent a letter of resignation. This was dated 27 October 1872.

8

He was evidently very disappointed and wrote a letter of resignation in which he did not conceal his feelings—

> I therefore now place at your disposal the appointment which I always valued as your gift to me . . . it is bitterly galling virtually to be requested to resign upon the unjust explanation given, after having constantly since the commencement of the working of the Nightingale Training School of nurses most strenuously endeavoured to smooth all asperities and to promote good feeling and harmony as far as I had the power or ability, always labouring under great difficulties. . . . I have less regret in relinquishing my office than I otherwise should have felt had it not been evident to me from your silence upon my last communication that my opinion is no longer valued. In taking my leave allow me to express my deep and sincere sense of gratitude for the many acts of kindness you have evinced towards me on various occasions both public and private, never to be erased from my memory.

After Dr Whitfield's resignation the task of arranging the lectures for the nurses was entrusted to Mr Croft, a surgeon who had recently been elected to the senior surgical staff at St Thomas's Hospital. Mr Croft was enterprising and enthusiastic in his efforts to instruct the nurses. He drew up a proper curriculum and submitted it to Miss Nightingale for her approval. He not only lectured, but he arranged for other members of the staff also to give lectures. He advised the nurses what books to read to supplement the lectures. He used to ask them questions, though, as Miss Crossland reported to her chief, the questioning was not always to the point nor vigorous enough. He wrote to Miss Nightingale that he hoped 'to become, as you would have me, an active and faithful comrade,' as in fact, he became. He also gave occasional clinical lectures at which the matron and the home-sister were expected to attend.

Mr Croft must indeed be regarded as the founder of the system whereby nurses are given a good elementary grounding in the main principles of medicine and surgery. He was conscientious and thorough and he consulted Miss Nightingale on every doubtful point. His lecture notes were printed. His ability and zeal delighted her, and on a scrap of paper which is still to be seen among her papers can be read the highest praise which anyone could hope to earn from Miss Nightingale: ' . . . before you were sent by Providence to guide us, for surgeons as well as saints are made in heaven': this must have referred to Croft. When in 1892, after nineteen years' service, he retired from the post of lecturer, he was presented with an inscribed silver bowl by the Council of the School, and he also received a letter of thanks from Miss Nightingale which pleased him mightily. As he put it—

> I am more proud of that written token from Miss Nightingale than of any other testimonial. Alas! that I did so little in 19 years and left so much undone for such a loveable and adorable leader.

With other members of St Thomas's staff Miss Nightingale had little to do. She was grateful to them for giving lectures to the nurses, but it is doubtful if she ever met any of them. Yet there were two members of the staff of whom she was severely critical, not on account of their professional distinction, for that was generally acknowledged, but in connection with a subject on which she was herself an authority—i.e. sanitation. These two men were Mr (afterwards Sir) John Simon, and Dr Bristowe, the well-known physician. Mr Simon, who was a distinguished surgeon and pathologist, had been made medical officer of health for the City of London in 1848, then in 1855 medical officer to the Board of Health and in 1858 was appointed adviser to the Privy Council when they took over the duties of the Board. To these important duties he brought a powerful and well-trained intellect and a mind of wide culture. He carried on the work begun by Chadwick, but his scientific training enabled him to take a wider outlook on the whole sanitary question. Miss Nightingale had no scientific training but held certain empirical sanitary doctrines tenaciously.

Among the enormous correspondence which she left behind, there is only one letter from Mr Simon, written when he was over eighty years of age. It may reasonably be inferred, therefore, that he never consulted her on any sanitary or hospital matter, as indeed he had no need to do. Whether she was in any way piqued by this we do not know, but there is evidence that she did not like

Simon, did not appreciate the splendid work he was doing, but rather belittled his achievements and occasionally tried to hinder his legitimate progress. One example will serve to show that she was not merely a passive opponent. On 2 April 1860 she wrote to Dr Farr—

> He [Mr Herbert] will speak to Milner Gibson about putting Sutherland on the Committee for the Congress (in order to hedge Simon).

Dr Farr himself, though he admired the ability of Simon, was not at this time very appreciative of his work.

The most serious attempt Miss Nightingale made to interfere with Simon's work occurred in 1864. One of the investigations sponsored by Simon was a report on the condition, sanitary and otherwise, of all the hospitals in the country. For this purpose he nominated Dr Bristowe a physician on the staff of St Thomas's Hospital and medical officer of health for Camberwell, and Mr Timothy Holmes, a surgeon on the staff of St George's Hospital. After reporting on the hospitals in this country they visited hospitals in Paris. Miss Nightingale must have had early and private intimation of this, for she promptly, too promptly as it happened, took action. She had gained so much by backstairs influence in Government circles that she had no hesitation in writing to Mr Robert Lowe, who had the power of nomination for the proposed task, to tell him that in her opinion better men might have been chosen for the task. This time she had mistaken her man. Mr Lowe replied promptly and firmly, justifying his choice. His first letter was dated 23 February 1864—

> My dear Miss Nightingale,
>
> Mr Holmes of St George's and Dr Bristowe of St Thomas's are employed to report on the hospitals of the United Kingdom and have only incidentally to visit the Paris hospitals. You wish we had taken 'better men.' Were you not rather premature in this wish, as you did not know who the men were. I should have been glad to have employed better if I could have found them. It gives me much pleasure to hear from you again.

Miss Nightingale wrote again soon after receiving this letter, and this time she made a direct attack on Simon. Lowe lost no time in sending her a spirited reply in which he not only defended Simon but made a challenging attack on Miss Nightingale's own views. His letter was dated 26 February 1864—

MY DEAR MISS NIGHTINGALE,

I should be glad to do anything in my power for the reform of hospitals but unhappily, my bolt is soon shot, and when I have laid the report which I have directed on the table of the House I have done all in my power.

I am sorry that you do not approve of Mr Simon, my official adviser. I have no pretensions to the knowledge which would enable me to form a judgement of his medical acquirements, but having had four years' experience of him I can say with great sincerity that he is singularly well informed with a great appetite for knowledge of all kinds and a most ardent zeal for sanitary reform as he understands it.

I cannot help feeling that you have met with those who have created an undue prejudice in your mind against him. The medical world has its factions as well as the political, and we should all cut strange figures if we were to be judged by the report of our antagonists. As a proof that Simon has not overlooked the subject of hospitals I may refer to pp. 18, 19, 36–40 of his report in 194 V [sic] on preventible disease, where he expatiates on the effects of ventilation and drainage on puerperal fever, pyaemia, and erysipelas.

Will you allow me to point out what appears to me to be an oversight in your book on hospitals? You speak of hospitals as unhealthy (in a bad sense) because there is a large percentage of deaths to beds. In one sense every hospital ought to be unhealthy, that is, the refuge for disease, and in that sense the healthier it is (that is the better it is conducted) the more unhealthy it will be.

Is it not rather in the number of patients received into the hospital in the course of the year, and the severity of the case, that the percentage of deaths to beds depends, and is it not quite unanswerable that a hospital may be unhealthy from bad management and yet show a small percentage of deaths because few people get to it? Before we infer the unhealthiness of a hospital from the percentage of deaths to beds, we ought to know how many people have occupied the beds in the course of the year.

It seems to me that this error vitiates the argument from statistics which is assumed to prove that the unhealthiness in a bad sense of the London hospitals is to that of the country hospital as 90 to 39. A better test I should have thought would have been the prevalence of hospital diseases. Pray excuse this long letter.

I have not of course shown your letter to Simon. Had I been able to do so he would, I do not doubt, have made a very different case for himself than I in my ignorance can do for him.

Believe me always in sincere respect

ROBERT LOWE.

Thus Mr Lowe carried the battle into the enemy's camp. Though Simon had nothing to do with this reply, the argument is likely to have been prompted by someone close to him, possibly Bristowe. The only other doctor who at that time had a large experience of inspection of hospitals was Dr Sutherland, and it is very likely that Miss Nightingale had him in mind when she wrote her letter of protest to Mr Lowe.

Miss Nightingale's opposition to Mr Simon did not diminish for some time. In September 1866 she wrote to Farr—

You know I am entirely recalcitrant as to your Mr Simon's merits. Mr Simon is an arrangement of the Privy Council for making the Bigger Body, which is a great quack, appear (to the lesser bodies who are little quacks) to know something. . . . But what makes me most frantic is that Mr Simon, who is pluralist in every sense of the word, never 'paye's de sa personne.' Bad as we are at the War Office, Poor Law Board and in India, we should never accept Mr Simon's second hand reports. We always inspect ourselves—in person. Now you will say I am a nuisance, and come under the Nuisance Removal Act; and Mr Simon, if you wrote to him will gladly put it in force against me. But I shall be the only nuisance Mr Simon will have ever removed.

The witty last sentence does not hide the animus in this letter. Mr Simon was at that time doing work which has stood the test of time and has made his name renowned in all sanitary circles. No one reading this letter, with its emphasis on first-hand information, would suspect that for six years Miss Nightingale had been entirely dependent upon others for information about the outside world.

Mr Simon became Sir John Simon in 1887, a rather tardy reward for outstanding services to his country. He had a high regard for Miss Nightingale. It is quite possible, and indeed likely, that he would hear of the letter written to Mr Lowe, but he harboured no animosity. In 1897, when he was old and nearly blind, he sent Miss Nightingale a charming letter (13 November 1897), accompanied by a copy of the new edition of his famous book, *English Sanitary Institutions—*

DEAR MISS NIGHTINGALE,

With apologies for my intrusion, which let me hope you will excuse when I plead that I am 81 years old, may I take the liberty of begging you to do me the honour of accepting from me the copy which I herewith send of the new edition of my *English Sanitary Institutions.* I am well aware that it can give you no new knowledge in its main subject matter; but incidentally it tells the story of what I have tried to do for the interests which you have so signally promoted; and believe me it is with deep reverence for your devotion to the course of life you have made your own, that I venture, in now preparing to leave the scene, to beg for a little place in your recollection.

My almost blindness has obliged me to delay till I could include in the note what I have to say on another subject, my very earnest thanks for the kindness you have acceded to my petition that my grand-niece, Jane Blake, might be admitted to the staff which is yours at my dear old hospital. I beg you to believe that I would not have recommended her to you unless I had sincerely believed that she would devote herself dutifully to the work; and it is my earnest hope that when her year's probation is completed she may be found not unworthy to fill a permanent place in the surgical service of the hospital. If you still sometimes (as I hope) find yourself able to see them, or some of them who are being educated under your influence, I would venture to beg you to let her be of the number and that she may be able to carry on with her through life the memory of one who will be her example.

Believe me, dear Miss Nightingale, with truer respect than my crippled handwriting can express,

ever your faithful servant,

JOHN SIMON.

That letter would surely soften any hardness of heart. We must hope that by this time they had become friends.

10

Sir Henry Wentworth Acland
and
The Registration of Nurses

DOCTORS ATTAINED a legal status by the Medical Act of 1858, whereby the General Medical Council was instituted and the Medical Register established. The nursing profession had to wait till 1919 before the General Nursing Council was created and the State Register for Nurses was set up. But for Miss Nightingale the gap between the two events might have been considerably shortened. It has long been known that she was strongly opposed to any form of registration for nurses, but, so far as I am aware, the active part she took in putting an end to the earliest attempt to institute a state registration of nurses has never previously been revealed. The story is to be gleaned from the correspondence between Miss Nightingale and Dr (afterwards Sir) Henry Acland, and from the minutes of the General Medical Council. Dr Acland was one of the original members of the General Medical Council.

Dr Acland attended professionally some of Miss Nightingale's relatives, and as early as 1867 he wrote asking her advice with regard to the training of nurses at the Radcliffe Infirmary, Oxford, where he acted as physician. About 1869 he wrote again asking her views concerning the training and certification of women in several occupations; to judge from her reply he must have supported the training of women doctors, and the granting of certificates of proficiency to nurses who had passed a certain examination. All her life Miss Nightingale was opposed to the granting of certificates of proficiency to nurses. Her reply to Dr Acland contained the following striking remarks—

'Had you asked me the same question fifteen or sixteen years ago before I had the experience I have had since, I should have fallen in eagerly with your project. . . . Experience then teaches me now (1) that nursing and medicine must never be mixed up. It spoils both. If the enemy wished to ruin our nurses in training at St Thomas's it would be by persuading me to accept your noble offer of a female special certificate (or any degree) for them. (and I can say quite unaffectedly that it is a noble and generous offer). If I were not afraid of being misunderstood I would almost say—the less knowledge of medicine a hospital matron has the better (1) because it does not improve her sanitary practice, (2) because it would make her miserable or intolerable to the doctors.

From this reply it would appear that Dr Acland already had the idea to try and persuade the General Medical Council to recognize a qualifying certificate for nurses, and that Miss Nightingale would have none of it. Nevertheless, he still kept in view the possibility of inducing the Council to do something to further the education of women in medicine, midwifery, nursing and pharmacy. Three years later (on 4 March 1872) at the General Medical Council he proposed, and Dr Stokes seconded, a motion—

that a Committee be appointed to consider and report whether the General Medical Council has power to make rules for the special education of women such as may entitle them to obtain a qualification to be certified by the Council; and that the Committee do further report for what purpose such qualifications, if any, should be granted, what are the most desirable means for educating, examining, and certifying in respect of them with special reference to midwifery, the management of medical institutions, dispensing and nursing.

This resolution was passed by the narrow majority of one vote.

Meanwhile, even before this resolution had been passed by the Council, Dr Acland had written to Miss Nightingale, giving her the text of the proposed resolution and asking for her opinion and advice. She gave it freely and frankly, and showed as clearly as possible that she disapproved of the whole business, with the exception of midwifery.

She was alarmed at the prospect of examination and certification in connection with nursing. Here are some of her arguments—

> Nursing does not come within the category of those arts (or sciences) which may be usefully 'examined' or 'certified' by the agency proposed. . . . There is nothing in my experience since 1865 but what has only confirmed this view, viz, that the proposed examination as far as nursing is concerned would be not only useless but mischievous. It is generally admitted now that examination in clinical subjects cannot be made from books. Nursing is not only an art but a character, and how can that be arrived at by examination? It cannot. These reasons appear to be final, do they not, as against any examination and registration by the Medical Council.

It will be seen that one of the main objections put forward against examination was that nursing was largely a matter of character. A slight concession was made in the following sentence—

> There might possibly arise the question—suppose any nurse-training committee, after sufficient experience should decide that such and such women had really the nurses' calling, it might become a question whether these should not be placed on the Register merely on certificate? i.e. without examination by the Council.

She thought that rules for the training of nurses could not be laid down by the Medical Council, and she also made it clear that in her opinion midwifery stood on a different plane from nursing. Finally, on the question of the management of medical institutions she made the following comment—

> I do not quite understand what is here contemplated. The superintendence of a medical institution as conducted by a woman includes sanitary knowledge, knowledge of management, administration, housekeeping, above all training and management of women both as to character and skill. To propose to examine in these things can scarcely come within the province of a Medical Council.

This criticism does not appear to have made a deep impression on Dr Acland, for the committee under his chairmanship continued their deliberations for a year, and it was only when their report had been provisionally drawn up that he again sought Miss

Nightingale's advice. On 23 March 1873 he wrote to her as follows—

> The Medical Council sits again this week. I am preparing a draft report for the committee on 'woman's education.' I venture to send the draft to you. I have many representations from various quarters as to the advisability of adopting some mode of licensing for the midwives and superintendent nurses. It seems to me that the time is quite come for thoroughly sifting and settling whether the Medical Council should or should not do it. This issue I hope to try this week. . . . It occurs to me that you may by chance object to some of my brief statements in the draft [note in red pencil by Miss N. 'I do'.] or be willing to supplement some deficiencies or give me some instructions as to your own wishes.' [Note by Miss N. 'There is no time.']

In spite of her marginal comment Miss Nightingale soon got to work and wrote out a series of suggestions and criticisms which she sent by special messenger to Dr Acland. She pointed out that midwives and dispensers were in an entirely different category from nurses and superintendents of medical institutions. She thought that 'a most effective impulse might be given to the education of midwives,' but on the question of what move should be taken in the matter of examining and registering nurses she very cleverly held up a mirror to him in the following ingenious way—

> I could fancy you, if you were asked, giving the following wise advice, or something like it.
>
> 'You are not yet in a position to move at all. You have no feet. What you ought to report to the Council is simply the information which you have collected—and the information collected is not sufficient to enable steps to be taken. If you attempt to walk without feet either you stand still or fall over' (so far Dr Acland).
>
> Would you not limit your report simply to a résumé of existing information,—cut out all advice. Ask the Council to continue the powers of the Committee. Before your report is printed or adopted I shall be obliged to you to give me full opportunity of looking it over as at present my views do not appear to be correctly represented.

This letter was written on 26 March. Acland replied next day and was obviously shaken by the criticisms of his report. He commented—

> It is clearly a big subject. I think the Medical Council will on the whole take it *au sérieux*, though some will endeavour to cast it aside

as unworthy. I think they will fail, and they certainly will if I have
enough self-control to delay recommendations this year as you advise.
This will certainly allow the Committee to take more trouble, if it
does not commit the Council.

The very next day (28 March) Acland sent Miss Nightingale
another revise of the report, with the added comment—

> It is of great consequence that the Committee should not flinch from
> making some report now.

Judging from that remark he must have been feeling very doubtful about the whole matter. She asked to see the final revision
before it was printed and he sent her a rather desponding letter—

> I received your packet this morning with not a little compunction.
> I fear I have given you much trouble. I shall be glad if in the end I do
> not displease you, though to be sure even then I shall probably believe
> I did not deserve it. Now I have modified the report as far as I could
> to meet your wishes. It is wonderfully cut down—and seems short
> to a marvel. But in this case I am sure half a loaf is better than no
> bread, and brown bread also better than none. This report will be a
> fulcrum for future work. I cannot but think it will be accepted. We
> have made the recommendation to be that the Committee (not the
> Council) should do certain things, mainly make further enquiries
> and to prepare the way for the direction of future efforts.

Reading through the correspondence one cannot fail to see that the
originally strong opinions of Dr Acland were overborne by the
still stronger conviction of Miss Nightingale, that the original
proposals were watered down, and that, at her suggestion, the
only definite action taken was to recommend the Council to
reappoint the Committee and ask them to make further inquiries.
The Council did not adopt the report nor express any opinion on
it. If the Council had adopted the recommendations of the report,
it is likely that standardization of the training, and registration of
nurses would have been established many years before they actually
took place.

The two main recommendations of the report were—firstly,
that the Committee should be empowered

> to enter into communication with any public institution in which
> there is provision for the education and examination of women as

midwives, dispensers, superintendents of nurses and medical institutions. Secondly, to consider and report whether and in what manner a public register of persons obtaining the qualifications might be kept.

An important paragraph was inserted which clearly indicated what the Committee had in mind—

The Committee, under these circumstances, are of opinion that in any future Bill for the amendment of the Medical Act, a clause should be introduced giving power to the Medical Council to register the qualifications of women acting as midwives, dispensers and superintendents of medical institutions. The register, they need hardly add, would be separate from the register of practitioners of medicine and surgery.

In the appendix to the report of the Committee there was printed a letter written by Mr Bonham Carter. Miss Nightingale complained that this letter was published without the permission of Mr Bonham Carter; at the same time she stated that she entirely agreed with the sentiments expressed in the letter. The following extract from this letter therefore may be taken as an expression of her own opinion—

All those who are interested in this subject ought, I am sure, to be much indebted to you for bringing it forward for consideration and discussion; that will at any rate have a beneficial effect; but I venture to think that, in the present condition of knowledge (or ignorance) which exists with regard to the proper system of training, and the very defective means of training at all, the time is not yet ripe for action on the part of the Council.

After Dr Acland had presented the report to the Council, he wrote to Miss Nightingale: 'I was attacked because it was so voluminous. I fear you will be displeased it is so meagre.' Miss Nightingale's marginal comment was 'What can he mean by this? I made him cut off much. I wanted him to cut off more.' The final letter of this correspondence came from Dr Acland ten days later when he told her that 'I shall proceed with caution. The subject must be and will be thoroughly sifted.' She wrote in the margin— 'I hope so.' The Committee was reappointed, but

in fact the subject was for the time finished. Miss Nightingale had
effectively stifled the attempt of the General Medical Council to
encourage the training and even the registration of nurses. Though
the project was never again raised in the General Medical Council,
Dr Acland still kept the registration of nurses in his mind as a
desirable thing. In 1874 he wrote a preface to a book by Miss
Florence Lees in which he included the following passage—

> The Medical Act of 1858 allows women to be registered as medical
> practitioners. It makes no provision for the registration of trained
> nurses, however complete their education and however great their
> skill, whether as midwives or nurses. Many accomplished women
> might reasonably desire the name as well as the function as superin-
> tendents of hospitals, or of ward sisters, or of nurses.
>
> At present they can have no such legal recognition of their
> qualification in either department, as is obtained by sisters who
> become schoolmistresses, or who are students and teachers of art.
> That this ought to be remedied can hardly admit of doubt; but it
> rests with the women of England to decide whether what is here
> advocated has their support as well as their approval.

But this advance was not destined to be accomplished while Miss
Nightingale was still alive.

In 1884 Dr Acland became Sir Henry Acland. Three years later
the question of the training and registration of nurses again came
into prominence, this time not from the General Medical Council
but from some of those whom it most concerned. In 1886 Mr
Burdett of the Hospitals Association tried to start a register for
nurses, but this attempt did not meet with the approval of many
nurses. In 1887 a number of nurses, led by Mrs Bedford Fenwick,
started the British Nurses' Association, having as its chief aim the
standardization of nurse-training and the registration of nurses.
Sir Henry Acland was a member of the Hospitals Association, but
when he found that Princess Christian was supporting the British
Nurses' Association he joined that body, which admitted medical
men as members. Miss Nightingale wrote to him saying she
was glad that he did not approve of the registration of nurses
'which the world is going mad about,' but in fact he seems to have
continued to be strongly in favour of some form of registration,

though he did not express too definite an opinion to Miss Nightingale.

To the end of her life she opposed the registration of nurses, and behind the scenes exercised great influence against it. Yet in July 1889 she wrote to Sir Henry: 'I have kept entirely out of the fray, as fray (though of course studying the sad Batrachyomachia and not withholding conviction).' By keeping out of the fray she could only have meant 'coming out into the open', because we know from her correspondence that she wrote or interviewed all the important persons whom she thought she could influence against registration.

When the British Nurses' Association applied for a charter, Miss Nightingale brought all the pressure she and her friends could furnish to influence the President of the Board of Trade (Sir Michael Hicks Beach) to refuse the granting of the charter. He refused to grant it. And so through every stage of the great fight she was the mainstay of the opposition against registration. She even wrote to Sir Henry Acland to say she would be willing, if considered necessary, to interview Princess Christian, who was president of the association that was advocating registration: 'I will see her if you like. The worst that can happen is that I shall be "floored." But I can only expound the hospitals' view.'

As time went on, she saw that she was fighting a losing battle, and the most she hoped for was to put off the fatal day till she had left the scene of battle. On 26 July 1890 she wrote to Sir Henry—

The mania for public examination of nurses appears to be spreading. . . . I have now letters from the foremost province (in Australia) in which the Governor . . . says that I shall be delighted to hear that two of their trained nurses have won the Gold Medal against the world! I need not comment on this to you.

In a letter written to Sir Henry on 28 April 1893 she expressed herself in words which show that she recognized that changes would soon be coming—

You ask me seriously for our conclusions and it would be base of me not to give them as you ask for them. Our conclusions are not final. On the contrary, we hope to start those of the next generation who

have practical experience in training and governing nurses—when
we are gone—through us to pass on to something higher than us.
But will the progress be assured or the reverse through R.B.N.A. or
public registers? We know that there are others who think the reverse,
who fear that whereas there is now enthusiasm among the nurses for
their own training schools, there will then be merely an interested
selfish regard as to which will 'get them on' the best, and a consequent deterioration in the training schools themselves, regarding only
who 'crams' best.

In February 1895 Sir Henry made one final indirect appeal to her.
He wrote saying that he had written a letter to the Empress
Frederick, and he continued—

I daresay you would not wholly approve. It was particularly to the
effect that it would be a great thing, not for England only but for
[those] that are sick and suffering if, now that the Queen and the
Princess Christian have as a fact established a recognized profession
of nurses, they should with you agree on what are the best conditions, and more, for that recognition.

He tried to improve the chances of a favourable reply by adding
a compliment—

Through you the practice of the profession of medicine has largely
changed in the last 40 years. It is quite recognized now that many
nurses are better informed on many important details than many
registered practitioners.

But it was too late to induce her to change her convictions.

Sir Henry Acland supported Miss Nightingale in her efforts to
maintain the Army Medical College and encouraged her whenever
there were doubts as to its continuance. He had the highest personal regard for her. On one occasion when he was asked to give
away some certificates to nurses and to deliver an address in the
East of London, he wrote to Miss Nightingale after the meeting:
'I had you always in mind in all I said.' He might have added 'and
did' in reference to everything connected with nursing.

Sir Henry was created a baronet in 1890. He died at Oxford in
1900.

Henry W. Acland.

9. Sir H. Wentworth Acland (1815–1900), Regius Professor of Medicine at Oxford from 1857 to 1894

(From a drawing by George Richmond, sculp. by Charles Hill)

10. Sir James Clark (1788–1870)
From a photograph in Queen Victoria's private collection

(' *The Practitioner*', *1897*)

II

Water-Cure Doctors

A VERY GOOD EXAMPLE of Miss Nightingale's summing up of the value of a method of treatment is furnished by her judgement on the, at that time, very popular 'water-cure' at Malvern. In 1848 she went with her mother, who had been advised to take the cure at Malvern, and four years later she went in like manner with her father to Umberslade Park, where he had been recommended to place himself under the care of Dr Johnson. She took notice of the persons who were undergoing the cure and summed up both their character and the worth of the treatment succinctly—

> The water-cure:—a highly popular amusement within the last few years amongst athletic invalids who have felt the *tedium vitae*, and those indefinite diseases which a large income and unbounded leisure are so well calculated to produce.

In spite of this biting criticism Miss Nightingale with singular acuteness observed that many people benefited from their stay at Malvern, and when, in 1858, as the result of prolonged overwork, and too little food and sleep, she began to feel exhausted, she chose to go there alone to try the effect of the water-cure. She undoubtedly felt some benefit, for in 1867 when again she was compelled to diminish her activities, she once more retreated to Malvern and put herself under the care of Dr Johnson.

Yet, while outwardly submitting to the cure, she was in no sense deluded into thinking it a cure-all, for, as her account clearly shows, she shrewdly estimated it at its true clinical worth.

It happened that in September 1860 Edwin Chadwick wrote to her, asking her opinion as to the value of the water-cure at Malvern for patients afflicted with early tuberculosis of the lungs. Here is her remarkable reply, dated 8 September 1860—

I make haste to answer your question as to my experience (as an old nurse) in the application of the water-cure to incipient consumption, especially as it regards so valuable a life.

(1) In incipient tuberculosis, when the object is to avoid local congestion, the water-treatment (not as a charm as English women take medicine but as part of a treatment) I have seen to be most effectual, the rest of the treatment being open air during the greater part of the day (riding or otherwise according to the patient's strength), bed-room ventilation at night, diet founded upon improved digestion, the result of the open air exercise—sometimes gentle gymnastics, mild cold-water sponging and little wet-sheet packing.

(2) Where tubercular deposit has begun I have seen cold-water treatment (especially in unskilful or careless hands) actually accelerate the local congestion and end. (a) I would not trust any woman (including myself) to say whether the patient is in a stage to require and to benefit by the cold-water cure—nor what it should be. This of course must be done by a doctor.

(b) I know no London doctor, except Sir James Clark, who would give an impartial opinion as to whether the patient should (or should not) go to a cold-water doctor. (c) I have seen a good deal of all the hydropathic doctors. Dr Gully of Malvern has the most genius but his practice is so large, his fortune so assured, that I have known him away for weeks and leave his patients to a third rate practitioner, and I have known him keep cases of phthisis (not from self-interest but from carelessness) to die at a miserable little lodging at Malvern instead of sending them away to an easier death at home or in a warmer climate. Dr Walter Johnson, a little strange scrubby boorish looking man is the most careful, impartial, disinterested, clever water-doctor I have known. (He is also at Malvern.) I would always trust him to send away a case (or not to treat it at all) if or when he thought it would be better elsewhere—as also to know if and when that period arrived. I am quite sure that life may be long rendered valuable by these means in incipient tuberculosis.

Mr Chadwick replied to this letter promptly. He seems to have been strongly attracted to this method of treatment, for in her next letter (14 September 1860) Miss Nightingale sounds a note of caution—

I think if I were you I should be extremely careful not to give such a name as yours, without qualification, to (a) hydropathic treatment, (b) Roman Bath [treatment].

(*a*) Practically I advocate exactly what I wrote to you about water-cure. But theoretically (and your name would give weight to any theory you chose to uphold) the hydropathic quackery is just like other quackery, an imperfect development of a certain form of treatment—hydropathy being only the name for drawing fees. The 'skin '(or hydropathy) theory has been put in practice in other ways; and has not achieved cure, shewing that it is the <u>whole</u> way of life, not the particular specific which brings about the <u>cure</u>. In my young days I perfectly remember another quackery which forbade the taking any more liquid than was necessary to support life—especially not a drop of <u>cold water</u> was to be drunk. The two specifics are 'much of a muchness.'

(*b*) 'The Roman Bath' now is only Mr Erasmus Wilson's adaptation of the Turkish . . .

With regard to drugs . . . until the British public is enlightened enough to pay the doctors for their knowledge and not for their drugs, the medical profession will be a base and not disinterested one. It will not be, as you say, a sanitary profession. Most medical men are obliged to trade in drugs to get a living. Whatever you can say to raise the national knowledge and feeling on the subject will be a national benefit. I went as near the wind as I could in my 'Notes on Nursing'. You can go much nearer. But I would take care if I were you to keep to principles, not to give particulars, which may be gainsaid or abused or misapplied.

Two days later she wrote still another letter on the water-cure, apparently in answer to yet another communication from Chadwick—

You and I do not mean the same thing by the 'water-cure.' I am not at all prepared to dispute 'that Mr Roebuck was 'built up at Malvern,' but does he think that if he had had Dr Gully at Ashley Place, Westminster, he would have built him up with any number of wet sheets? It is because Dr Gully is a brave and sensible man and says 'It is I and Malvern must do it' that he succeeds. But would it not be better to call this the 'absence from Parliament' cure or the 'quiet life and exercise cure'? My objection is really only a practical one. The quack name has done mischief. It has in a measure prevented, as all quack idolatry (of any specific) does, the recognition of the hygienic treatment of disease. Admit fully the utility of water, hot and cold, as an adjunct to recovery. But it is not all.

(*b*) How wicked it would be in me to disparage what is (unwisely) called the 'hydropathic' treatment. But this treatment, so humane because so successful, includes much more than water (either hot or cold or both). Take Mr Roebuck's case. There was absence from Parliament, absence from head excitement, absence from night hours, proper diet, quiet life, exercise, fresh mountain air, and different kinds of bathing. In my own case which I only mention because it is that of thousands, I recognize, just as much as I recognize that 11 oz of carboniferous food are necessary for a man in health, that I should not be here were it not for Malvern. In August 1857, after my work at the Royal Sanitary Commission, and after four weeks of anxiety and exertion, I was told that my life was not worth 24 hours purchase —and I knew it too. I owe three years of (not useless) life to the water-cure at Malvern, altho' it could not cure.

(c) Just as little, however, does water, *per se*, as calomel e.g. in pulmonary phthisis: I know that water cannot arrest it; cannot even delay the diseased action. But gentle gymnastics with good air and water, can—dumb-bells if the patient's strength permits, horse exercise if the patient can bear it, or other modifications which a wise and careful 'hydropathic' doctor introduces. But these cannot be called 'water-treatment' exactly. Let us have 'nature instead of drugs.' But don't let us erect or degrade water into the status of a drug.

(d) Again I am not at all prepared to dispute (as the doctors say) that the water-cure gets out mercury and other deleterious drugs thro' the skin. But all sufficient perspiration, whether excited by friction or other means, does the same—and the true sanitary conclusion is—don't take the mercury etc. I don't disparage the wet-sheet packing. I know it has saved many lives in fever. I am sure it saved mine. I believe to a weary rheumatic labourer, before or after he has been at his day's work, it would be even more helpful than the Turkish bath.

(e) Russian, Turkish, Roman, hot air, and vapour baths are all under the same category as Hydropathy; none is a specific, all good as part of a Hygienic system. Praise them all in their places—all these forms of baths, That is all I contend for.

And seldom has such a contention been so eloquently, clearly and correctly justified. The common sense and medical acumen shown in these letters make it abundantly clear that Miss Nightingale had the correct idea of the *modus operandi* of the water-cure treatment. She recognized that some patients suffering from early pulmonary tuberculosis were benefited by open air and gentle exercise, and in that she was well ahead of the medical opinion of her time.

Moreover, she was wise enough to leave it to the doctors to judge when such treatment would be beneficial.

One of the bills which she received from Dr Johnson has come down to us. It shows that the treatment was not expensive.

Bill due to Dr Johnson at Malvern Bury House dated 31 Oct 1857.

Treatment	10 days	£6.	0.	0.
	Fires.		7.	6.
	Candles.		1.	6.
	Servant, one day.		3.	0.
		6.	12.	0.

12

Two Surgeons at St Bartholomew's Hospital

SIR JAMES PAGET (1814–1899)

MISS NIGHTINGALE always spoke of Sir James Paget with the utmost respect. Whatever derogatory remarks she made about the medical and surgical professions, and they were many, she always made an exception of Mr Paget. She thereby showed her penetrating judgement by her recognition of a great and good man.

So far as one can gather from documents, she first came to know Mr Paget in 1859 when he treated one of her maids for some affection of the hand. At that time she was in the midst of her campaign for getting hospitals to make uniform returns of the diseases treated in their wards, and she took the opportunity, while thanking him for his attention to her maid, to ask him if he would help by filling up some of her statistical forms which she had had specially prepared for hospitals. He consented, and within a week he received the forms, with (in Miss Nightingale's usual careful manner) directions as to the manner in which they should be filled up. Three months later (31 January 1860) she wrote gleefully to Dr William Farr saying that she had heard from Mr Paget to the effect that at St Bartholomew's Hospital they had appointed a registrar, adopted the standard forms, and expected in due time to send her the results. A year later Mr Paget sent her the fruit of the first year's registration, which she forwarded to Dr Farr for comment. He did not reply promptly enough for her, so on 20 April she wrote—

> You have not criticized my Apostle's statistics for me—and Paget and I are waiting breathless upon your voice. You have not even returned me the copy to comfort myself with.

Farr thereupon replied: 'The sight of the St Bartholomew's report is refreshing and is a testimonial, not to be despised, to the power of perseverance.' Whether he meant the perseverance of Miss Nightingale or of Mr Paget he did not make quite clear. Miss Nightingale immediately passed the compliment on to Mr Paget and told him that Bart's had the credit of having produced the first hospital statistical report worth having.

Mr Paget continued conscientiously to return the annual statistics, which were sent on by her to Dr Farr, sometimes with a facetious note, as on April 1865—

> I send you St Bartholomew tho' no doubt you have received a copy. Please to return it to me with your remarks. I think the Saint deserves the greatest credit. But before I praise the Saint and worship at his shrine I should like to have your judgement whether there is anything more he ought to do before he is canonized by us (which you know is a much more critical thing than being canonized by Rome).

Farr's reply was brief—

> Bartholomew have given us a real contribution to medical science which deserves careful study. The Saint can afford to tell us how many of the cases on p 6 terminated fatally.

In 1856, in a passage severely critical of doctors in general, Miss Nightingale made an exception of Paget—

> Mr S not perhaps more than, but in common with doctors in general (with some splendid exceptions of which I put Mr Paget at the head) has, during the last few years, been bringing down medicine, including sanitary science, from a profession to a trade, that is, to sell an article called a prescription (or an operation) to the sick individual, said to be for his health, etc.

In 1887 Sir James Paget, the Duke of Newcastle and Sir Rutherford Alcock were appointed Trustees of the Women's Jubilee Fund which had been subscribed to celebrate the Jubilee of Queen Victoria's reign. Mr William Rathbone acted as honorary secretary to the Trustees and was no doubt also their trusted adviser. The decision was taken to use the Fund to help the development of district nursing, though for some time the exact form the scheme would take was doubtful. Both Sir James Paget and

Mr Rathbone (independently) kept Miss Nightingale informed of the decisions which were taken. At first Sir James said that in any scheme they would employ only certificated nurses—a statement which rather worried Miss Nightingale since St Thomas's Nursing School did not then grant their pupils a certificate of proficiency. On 5 November 1887 Sir James paid her a visit and gave a full account of the decisions of the Trustees; she promptly transmitted the gist of their conversation to Mr Rathbone—apparently not knowing that Mr Rathbone was acting as honorary secretary to the Trustees—

> I received a visit from Sir James Paget yesterday afternoon. The scheme of which they decided the bare outline on Thursday has gone to the Queen! (through the Duke of Westminster to Sir H. Ponsonby). She is to decide, and then remit it back to the Committee of Advice, if approved in its outline, for them to work it out in its parts.

She then gave a detailed account of their conversation in which the details of the scheme were more fully discussed, and she ended the letter—

> It is a singular advantage to have a conversation with Sir James Paget, because his perceptions are so quick and honest, he is not an advocate and he brings out of the rich stores of his experience things to support any true view—even with large bonuses he said the shareholders got the lion's share in ordinary Insurance Companies. I do not trouble you with what I said. Sir James asked to come again. I hope you will think things look more hopeful. God has taken the thing in hand, it appears.

The next year, 1888, when the British Nurses' Association had been founded and was agitating for a more uniform training of nurses and some standard form of qualifying examination, Miss Nightingale, who was strongly opposed to such developments, discussed the matter with Sir James Paget. She informed him that many hospitals were much opposed to the policy of the Nurses' Association, and in a letter to Dr Acland she commented—

> Sir James Paget seemed refreshed and rejoiced at this, instead of deprecating it. And all through, in his wise (as you say), gentle, terse, and witty way he seemed entirely inclined towards the 'row' and the clash of swords.

It is likely that Miss Nightingale unconsciously interpreted Sir James's views according to her own feelings, for it is difficult to imagine anyone less inclined to the 'clash of swords' than Sir James. There is no doubt, however, that he had a great admiration for Miss Nightingale. In acknowledging a copy of her *Notes on Hospitals* he wrote: 'It appears to me to be the most valuable contribution to sanitary science in application to medical institutions that I have ever read.' And of her *Notes on Nursing* he wrote: 'I am ashamed to find how much I have learnt from the Notes, more, I think than from any other book of the same size that I have ever read.'

There is one other reference to Sir James among her papers. On the occasion of the renewed application for a Charter by the Nurses' Association the matter was referred to the Privy Council for adjudication. Each side had influential backing. Miss Nightingale ridiculed the methods whereby the supporters of the Charter gained their medical adherents—

> In all my strange life through which God has guided me so faithfully (O that I had been as faithful to Him as He to me) this is the strangest episode of all—to see a number of doctors of the highest eminence giving their names to what they know nothing at all about. Sir James Paget told me himself that the names were asked for at a Court Ball —following each other like a flock of sheep; to see their Council of Registration made up of Sirs, only one of whom knows anything about nurse-training (Sir James himself asked me, why can't nurses lodge out, as students do!) to see these able good and shrewd men ignoring that such a thing is sure to fall into a clique.

It must be remembered that the views here given as those of Sir James are coloured by Miss Nightingale's own personality.

SIR WILLIAM SAVORY

The British Nurses' Association, which had for its object the raising of the status of nurses by standardizing training and establishing a register of qualified nurses, admitted medical men as members. One of the most prominent of the medical members was one of the surgeons on the staff of St Bartholomew's Hospital, Sir William Savory, at that time President of the Royal College of Surgeons and a well-known speaker and teacher. He presided at the second meeting of the Association on 13 February 1888. Princess Christian was present, as also were Sir Joseph Lister, Sir Dyce Duckworth, Sir Henry Acland and others. Savory had no doubts as to the merits of the objects of the Association. In his address he stated—

> The cause we have before us is so good and strong that it needs no advocacy from those who recognize the necessity of good nursing for the sick. In the first place a system of registration by a legally authorised body will secure a guarantee to all that those who appear on the register are qualified to take charge of cases.

Among Miss Nightingale's papers are some notes which she put together soon after this meeting and which were meant for Sir William Savory. We do not know whether Sir William asked her advice or whether she volunteered her views on the subject. We do not even know whether the memorandum ever reached him, but the probability is that such a carefully drawn-up argument would be despatched. The arguments are those which Miss Nightingale repeated again and again during the many years in which she contended against the certification and registration of nurses. We give the notes just as they were written down—

1. Don't attempt a General Register or a General Association for the Kingdom. Competing registers most desirable. Competition most important. Limit yourself at first to a Metropolitan Register. (The wider it is, the more difficult of supervision) 'Charter' or amalgamation, partial or otherwise, may follow. Have no centralization of business of that sort at present, with the very defective means of supervision that there are, very dangerous to form any register at all except on the narrowest lines. Nothing but a directory, nothing more than the list of certificated nurses with the training schools in which they have been trained, limiting it strictly to the date at which the certificates were given.

A medical man is not a nurse or an administrator. You would not take your medical man from the register, but the public will take its nurses. To the doctor complaining, she is on the register, the register places the secondary first, the first in the secondary place.

2. Training schools at present must not be certified. (Would you inspect the training schools? Then do you think they would admit 2 or 3 medical men of a self constituted body to say whether they are fit? A leading school which considers that it has given its certificate

does not choose that its certificate shall be revised by a self-constituted body, and has declined the register).

No sufficient standard what a training school ought to be.

No body constituted or capable of being constituted to lay down that standard at present.

1a. Essential difference between register of nurses and of doctors or even midwives? Character only to be ascertained by most recent evidence of confidential communication. Is this to be kept up by the official machinery in times subsequent to admission? It is the life approves the nurse. A few years after the medical man has been registered he himself may be as worthless as his diploma.

3. No public examination. Everybody with practical knowledge of a T.S. [training school] knows that the public examination, which must ignore all practical skill and all the moral qualities, put the primary test last and the secondary (last) first, makes that which is purely secondary the important essential thing. Is not the exam. test absolutely inefficient and misleading? Our marks in an examination count for little in our estimation of a nurse.

Preposterous that the scheme for establishing a register should exclude the managers of a hospital. Matron to be primarily responsible for the conduct and efficiency of a nurse.

Liverpool certificates have to be returned to be re-signed or initialled, or fresh-issued or expired periodically. They have to be re-signed triennially. What is proposed with regard to register?

We have been unable to find any letter from Sir William in reply to this memorandum, but he continued to support the movement in favour of the registration of nurses. A careful reading of these notes makes it clear that Miss Nightingale's views on registration were undergoing development. She already makes the admission that some form of registration may be necessary, but recommends that it should be started on a small scale.

The reader will find it interesting to compare Miss Nightingale's views on the examination of nurses with those she held equally strongly on the need for examination of the students at the Army Medical College. In the latter case she thought the examination was an excellent test of merit for use in posting candidates. She would not permit any discretionary powers to the Director-General, who presumably would also have taken into consideration the character of the individual.

13

Other Medical Friends

SIR JAMES CLARK. SIR WILLIAM BOWMAN. DR PATTISON WALKER. DR ELIZABETH BLACKWELL. DR JOHN SHAW BILLINGS. SIR JAMES Y. SIMPSON. DR PINCOFFS

SIR JAMES CLARK (1788–1870)

SIR JAMES CLARK is best known as the medical adviser of Queen Victoria. He deserves equally well to be known as the doctor who played an important part in freeing Miss Nightingale from the tyranny of her family. When she returned from Kaiserswerth she had already loosened the fetters which bound her, but her sister Parthenope and her mother made a last desperate effort to bind her to their orbit once more. Parthenope worked herself up into a frenzy to such an extent that Sir James, who was both a friend as well as the medical adviser of the family, gave it as his opinion that she was on the verge of a mental breakdown. He warned the family that it was in the best interest of both sisters that they should separate. He undoubtedly gave Florence that mental and moral support which enabled her to realize the necessity of cutting adrift from the family if she were to fulfil her destiny. In 1852 she had written—

> I am vibrating between irritation and indignation at the state of suffering I am in, and remorse and agony at the absence of enjoyment I promote in them. . . . I have been so long treated as a child that I can hardly assert this even to myself. It is with the greatest effort that I can reach it. . . . I must expect no sympathy from them.

With the support of Sir James Clark, however, she achieved freedom, and in the next year obtained the post of matron at the small hospital in Harley Street as proof of her emancipation.

She never forgot the debt she owed to Sir James, and so long as he lived she consulted him and confided in him almost as if he were an adopted father. When she returned from the Crimea full of her great purposes, it was Sir James who went with her to Balmoral and introduced her to Queen Victoria and the Prince Consort. When she succeeded in obtaining the appointment of a Royal Commission she went to some trouble to make sure that Sir James was one of the nominated members of the Commission. She well knew that he would support her views on the Commission. Later, when in 1857 an expeditionary force was being fitted out to send to China, it was by friendly intervention of Sir James that Miss Nightingale was able to influence the Director-General so that every possible medical precaution should be adopted; it was certainly unlikely that Sir Andrew Smith would have welcomed a direct approach from his former critic.

In the matter of the Army Medical School Sir James was of the greatest assistance. He helped her to draw up the regulations for the School, and she always kept him informed of the various setbacks which occurred from time to time. At one moment she was optimistic, at another depressed. In November 1858 she wrote to him joyfully—

I do not entertain the least doubt of the School being carried—and by nature and experience a sanguine mind having been denied me, it is not from sanguineness I think so.

A few years later she was in despair about everything—

The Army Medical Department is going to rack and ruin as fast as it can: as I have played my last card; I now think the only thing to be done is to revert to your proposal of another Royal Commission.

She discussed with him the appointment of the professors at the Medical School, and even told him what she thought the duties of a pathologist should be—

Pathologists are apt to get into the way of considering the main end of such a school to be that of making good pathological preparations. But if the Chatham School produces many pathological preparations you must report it to the Statistical Congress as bad. Pathology is doubtless essential. But the aim of our Army School is the prevention of disease, not the record of the harm disease has done.

When the Nightingale School for training nurses was founded in 1860 she took care that Sir James Clark should be one of the Council of management, while, on the other hand, when Queen Augusta of Prussia paid a visit to England in 1867, it was Sir James who, on behalf of Queen Victoria, arranged an interview between the royal visitor and Miss Nightingale. We have already seen how Sir James was the means of conveying to Queen Victoria the request from Miss Nightingale that Her Majesty should lay the foundation-stone of the new St Thomas's Hospital.

Sir James Clark was a constant source of encouragement to Miss Nightingale, and she must have felt his loss deeply when, at the ripe age of eighty-two years, he passed away in 1870.

SIR WILLIAM BOWMAN (1816–1892)

The most distinguished British ophthalmic surgeon of the mid-Victorian era was Dr (afterwards Sir) William Bowman. Dr Bowman was appointed assistant surgeon to King's College Hospital in 1840, and six years later he was elected to the staff of the Royal London Ophthalmic Hospital (Moorfields). He took an interest in the training of nurses and with Dr Bentley Todd was associated in the foundation, in 1844, of the St John's House for training nurses. He first met Miss Nightingale in 1853 when she was superintendent of nursing in the Harley Street hospital for gentlewomen. He did not fail to recognize her ability and in 1854 sought to obtain her services for the larger field of acting as Superintendent of Nurses at King's College Hospital. She had an admiration for Dr Bowman and had serious thoughts of applying for the post, but the Crimean War intervened and on her return she had other objects in view. She wrote to Dr Bowman from Scutari and when the nurse-training school was founded asked him to serve on the Council. He continued to serve after he was created a baronet in 1884, and to the end of his life maintained his interest in that institution.

Dr Bowman at one time (in 1861) tried to bring about some link between the Nightingale Fund and St John's House, but nothing came of this. The correspondence about this contains a few comments made by Miss Nightingale which are of some interest. She criticized the nursing at King's College Hospital, and added—

> The Bishop is consecrating the nursing which leads to churchyards with as much apparent zeal as bishops are said to consecrate the churchyard itself.

In another letter written to Dr Sutherland, she said: 'If either you or Dr Bowman were half as reasonable as Miss Jones I should be a happy woman.'

It was in connection also with the question of St John's House that she wrote to Dr Bowman a confidential letter in one part of which she asked him to burn the letter, and in another part requested him to return it. He returned it to her with a note that he did so 'on your own order.'

DR PATTISON WALKER

Dr Pattison Walker, from whose letters we have already quoted, was a medical officer in the Indian Army who introduced himself to her in a manner most suitable to enlist her sympathy and help. On 30 December 1863 he wrote to her—

> MADAM,
>
> As a medical officer of eighteen years standing I am desirous of returning from furlough with such information as may enable me to aid in the reduction of sickness and mortality in the Army, by performing my individual duty more efficiently and by helping to spread a knowledge of the progress already made as well as of those principles which may be considered as established.

Miss Nightingale was very pleased with this serious-minded appeal and referred him to the Indian Sanitary Commission's report as giving the best account of sanitation in India. His zeal appears to have been very quickly rewarded, for in 1864 he was appointed Sanitary Commissioner for Bengal, though unfortunately within a year he was compelled to resign that post on account of ill-health. For some years Miss Nightingale consulted him on various matters. Shortly after his appointment as Commissioner she wrote asking information about Delhi boils, and added—

> This is just one of the cases with which your Commission could effectually deal. The causation of boils is very little understood. If you could contrive a careful enquiry to be made to find out the cause at Delhi and remedy the evils much good might arise to the Service.

But the fact that the Delhi boil was caused by a protozoon was not discovered till many years later, and its successful cure by injections of antimony salts was not discovered till later still.

In 1868 Pattison Walker sent her a long account of his work in India which greatly pleased her—

> Your letter was as amusing to me as White of Selborne, as touching as Sterne, and you are as zealous as Mr Chadwick himself on sanitary matters with a poetry quite beyond Mr Chadwick.

In that same letter she added a typical Nightingale touch—

> When the Parliamentary session was over I 'disappeared' and would not give my address. I told the War Office I was going to Ephesus because I much preferred it to fighting W.O. beasts.

Her final words were an indirect appeal for sympathy which she frequently made: 'It is also 11 years this very day since I was taken ill with the illness from which I have never risen again.' The letter was dated 10 August 1868. The correspondence appears to have ceased then, or at least there are no further letters available.

DR ELIZABETH BLACKWELL

Miss Nightingale was more interested in nurses than in women doctors, but she was very friendly with Dr Elizabeth Blackwell, the first woman doctor to be put on the English Medical Register. In 1851 she invited Miss Blackwell to stay with her at Embley, and even expressed a wish that they might work together. Looking at the big house in which they were staying, Miss Nightingale told her friend that she had often imagined how it could be adapted as

11. Sir William Bowman (1816–92)

(From an engraving in the possession of the Royal Society of Medicine)

12. Florence Nightingale in her old age

(From a photograph by Mr Payne which appeared in 'The Sphere' in August, 1910)

a hospital and in her own mind had even determined how the beds should be placed!

At a later date, in February and March 1859, when the scheme for the nurse-training school was being outlined and no hospital had yet been decided upon, Miss Nightingale tried to persuade Miss Blackwell to take the post of superintendent in the new institute. Elizabeth wrote to her sister Emily: 'We conversed very earnestly about the nursing plan in which she wished to interest me.' As it happened, Miss Blackwell was not willing to take the post; one reason was that she wished also to do some private practice, which would not be compatible with the occupation of such a post. There was also the fact that Dr Whitfield was decidedly against such a scheme. He wrote: 'I do not think that you could find any one English lady capable of undertaking all that you require. Even if it was desirable it is hardly possible that Miss E. Blackwell could.' A possible third reason was that Miss Blackwell had a strong will and firm convictions on many subjects and she might have foreseen difficulties in dealing with another lady of equal strength of convictions. Anyway the scheme fell through, somewhat to Miss Nightingale's disappointment.

They kept in touch with each other during the rest of their lives, which ended in the same year—1910.

In 1871 Miss Blackwell was interested in an organization called the National Health Society, which had as its object the spreading of knowledge on sanitation and the methods of preserving health. She wished to have Miss Nightingale on the General Council of the Society, as indicated by the opening sentence of her letter—

I have begun what will be to me a serious life work and I want to know whether you will approve and be on our General Council.

The final sentence showed that they had similar ideals—

Dear friend, the never ceasing effort to make God's laws the rule of life seems to me the only thing worth living for; and I do long to render good service to my dear native land.

We do not know what success her appeal met with, for the reply from Miss Nightingale is not available.

About the same time Dr Blackwell wrote to Florence Nightingale asking her advice about the evidence which should be given before the Commission considering the Contagious Diseases Acts. Miss Blackwell had promised to give evidence to the effect that she thought compulsory physical examination was unjustified and cruel, and she thought that it might be a suitable opportunity to put forward suggestions which might remedy the evil which the Act was meant to mitigate. She asked for suggestions from Miss Nightingale and offered some herself for Miss Nightingale's approval.

Twelve years later, in March 1883, she once more wrote to Florence Nightingale with reference to the founding of a midwifery school. A small ladies' committee had considered the question and come to the conclusion that medical men would never organize such a school, so plans were drawn up for the formation of a school on a very moderate scale. The end of the letter was again on a very confidential note—

> You see therefore, dear friend, that we are very far yet from being able to put your admirable plans into force; but they will be a valuable guide for future work, I hope, and I am sure it will encourage future workers to know of the deep and lifelong interest you have taken in this subject.
>
> A confidential word about myself. I thought my work was done when I left my 'Moral education of the Young' as a legacy to my successors. But not so. A new and peculiar work has opened before the first woman physician that, as far as I can see, no one else is able to do. It is the education of men as well as women in true instead of false sexual physiology. Of course this is only the hidden gist of my work—the ways in which it must be worked out are various.

It was about this time that she once more visited her friend in South Street. Ishbel Ross, in her *Child of Destiny* comments on this meeting—

> Neither one understood any longer what the other one did, but the warmth of their friendship lingered. Elizabeth saw that Florence was changing—she was softening down. Her remarks had lost their bite. Her cynical face was turning bland. She was growing in bulk, she smiled more often, but she was worried now about the Indian Army, a subject which was soon to occupy Elizabeth too.

When first she knew Dr Blackwell, Miss Nightingale had a poor opinion of the medical capabilities of women doctors. But as the years went by, her opinion of women as doctors improved; she acknowledged that they could fulfil an important role as accoucheurs, and towards the end of her life, as is well known, she went still further and chose to be medically attended by a well-known woman doctor, Miss May Thorne.

DR JOHN SHAW BILLINGS

Miss Nightingale's reputation as a sanitarian and as an expert on the designing of hospitals brought to her many requests from all parts of the world for advice on, and criticism of, hospital plans. When the Johns Hopkins Hospital was about to be built, her advice was sought by Dr J. Shaw Billings, who, as is well known, played a large part in the building of that famous hospital. On 23 October 1876 he sent the following letter to Miss Nightingale—

> I take the liberty of sending to you through Mrs Wardroper who has very kindly consented to forward the package, a set of sketch plans for a hospital to be constructed at Baltimore U.S. under the terms of the Johns Hopkins Trust. With this hospital are to be connected a training school for nurses, a convalescent hospital, an orphan asylum and some other things. I am now on my way to the Continent and shall return towards the end of November, spending a day or two in London on my way to the U.S. Knowing as I do the great interest you take in such subjects, I shall consider it as a great favour if before my return you will if your health permits examine these plans and the two pamphlets which accompany them and let me know what you think of them. They are only sketch plans and I desire criticism before going further. I am with great respect very sincerely yours
>
> JOHN S. BILLINGS.

Miss Nightingale promptly showed the plans to Dr Sutherland and asked his opinion of them. He was not favourably impressed by them and suggested that Miss Nightingale should not criticize them but, as Abernethy did to his patients, refer them to her writings on the subject of hospitals. This would not satisfy her, however, and she promptly set to work, examined the plans thoroughly, and forwarded her suggestions to Dr Billings, as may be gathered by the second letter he sent her, dated 4 December 1876—

> I have the honour to acknowledge the receipt of your letter of Dec. 2 enclosing 12 sheets of notes on the Johns Hopkins Hospital plans, and I desire to express my sincere personal thanks for this favor. Your remarks shall be laid before the Trustees as soon as I return to America, and I feel quite sure that they will be very greatly interested in and influenced by your criticisms. I do not think it probable that I should do otherwise than agree with them (the suggestions).
>
> The labour and expense of conducting an hospital built in this general plan I fully appreciate, as also the complications which arise in trying to cut off all service rooms from the ward. I infer from your note that you may not have received a copy of a book containing five different plans for the hospital published by the Trustees about 9 months ago. I am quite sure that a copy was sent to you. The first of the plans in that book I prepared and in it I think many of your objections were avoided. If you have not seen it I shall make sure that a copy is sent to you.
>
> That at first but one or two blocks should be built is precisely what I think. But I will not attempt now to comment upon your notes, nor indeed do I think it probable that I should do otherwise than agree with them. The copies of plans sent you were intended to be kept by you and other plans will be sent to you hereafter. If you have not the volume containing the five plans and will let me know it I will have it sent.
>
> For the next 9 days my address will be care of Brown, Shipley and Co, Founders Court, Lothbury, London. After that Surgeon General's Office, Washington, D.C., U.S.A. I leave London by the 5th inst. for Leeds, Edinburgh etc and sail on the 16th. Again thanking you for your criticism I remain
>
> very respectfully and truly yours,
JOHN S. BILLINGS, M.D., U.S.A.

I have made inquiries of the Johns Hopkins Hospital and was informed that there was no record referring to the suggestions made by Miss Nightingale. Inquiries at the British Museum elicited the information that their copy of the book containing the five plans for the Johns Hopkins Hospital was destroyed by enemy action during the war of 1939–45.

SIR JAMES Y. SIMPSON

In 1869 Florence Nightingale was extremely interested in the training of midwives and the structure of maternity hospitals. At that time the cause of puerperal fever was not known and it was generally believed to be due to bad sanitation in the lying-in hospitals. Among those from whom she asked information was Sir James Y. Simpson. In a letter dated 13 June 1869 he gave her his views on 'hospitalism' and what measures should be taken to combat the high mortality in hospitals. His long letter was written in green ink while he was away from home at a confinement. In it he made an interesting original suggestion—

> Mr Norton of Liverpool, the great builder of iron churches, houses, etc, is working at present at the problem of making one storey iron hospitals; and he hopes to construct them greatly cheaper than when made of stone and lime. I have a great fancy to line them internally with a layer of vegetable charcoal which is quite cheap and burns off all effete animal matter. It could be placed between the outside iron wall and a wire grating internally, and the grating could be painted, etc.

We have no information as to whether this plan was ever tried.

DR PINCOFFS

Among Miss Nightingale's miscellaneous correspondence there are two letters written to Dr Pincoffs, whom she had met in the period of the war either at Scutari or the Crimea. Apparently he had written to her soon after her return to England, asking permission to refer in some publication to her work. She replied (26 August 1856): 'being naturally unwilling to make myself prominent [I] entreat that my name may not be introduced in connection with it in any communication to a public paper.'

The next year Dr Pincoffs must have asked something about the Hospital for Gentlewomen in Harley Street, for her letter gives details about the cases which she saw there. It shows her powers of clinical observation—

> The cases, while I was there [were] almost invariably hysteria or cancer. I gained a very curious experience while there in managing the former class of cases. I had more than one lunatic. I think the deep feeling I have of the miserable position of educated women (or rather of half-educated women in England) was gained while there; but I would not undertake it again. I would begin much nearer the source. For the fancy cases I had were to organic cases as 4 to 1; physicians were of little help; they rather made the women worse (though all first rate) for the patient looked upon medical attendance as a luxury. . . .

It would have been interesting to know how Miss Nightingale dealt with these women who had no organic disease, but, according to her account, were suffering from hysteria.

14

Miss Nightingale's Invalidity

Miss Nightingale lived to the age of ninety years. During more than half this period she lived the life of an invalid, and on several occasion both she and her friends, medical and lay, thought that she had but a short time to live. What could be the nature of the illness or disability which permitted her to do an immense amount of work but confined her to her room and caused her to eat her meals in solitude? From 1857 to 1910 she lay in bed or on a couch or sat in an invalid-chair most of the time, interviewed her relatives, friends and visitors one at a time, and frequently communicated with her colleague Dr Sutherland by means of notes sent from her room to another room in which he remained during this curious, this unique method of communication. On 25 July 1870 she sent a note to Dr Sutherland (who was apparently in a neighbouring room): 'I cannot write another word today. If you come tomorrow I may be able to see you. We have much to decide.'

On 17 August 1864 Edwin Chadwick, the eminent sanitarian, wrote to her: 'Among other results of your malady I deplore the inability to see you and talk over matters of mutual interest in half an hour which would require the labour of a day to write.' She never would see more than one visitor at a time, nor more than three or four in a day.

Yet during the long time that she was confined to her room she did an immense amount of work, reading blue-books, collecting volumes of information, writing countless letters, often of great length, putting together elaborate memoranda and tables of statistics, and penning innumerable notes, many of which are preserved in the one hundred and fifty large volumes in the British Museum, not to mention other documents elsewhere. Her correspondence kept her in touch with statesmen, eminent doctors, matrons of hospitals, nurses, relatives and friends, and showed the working of an alert intellectual mind. The work she did has left a permanent mark on the medical and surgical professions in this country, on the sanitary condition of India, and on the Army Medical Service. What kind of disease could physically disable in such a curious way a woman who appeared to be resistant to most of the ordinary organic diseases?

The answer to this question can only be surmised after consideration of the early life of the patient, or, in medical parlance, the past history of the case.

Florence Nightingale was the younger of two daughters of William and Frances Nightingale. (Mr Nightingale was a rich landowner whose land yielded considerable mineral royalties.) The younger daughter was born in Florence in 1820. Her father was a well-educated man of high intelligence but not of strong determination. Her elder sister and her mother both had strong wills and domineered over Florence; they both enjoyed the excitements of a society life. Florence was of an entirely different nature, introspective, serious-minded, reflective, and rarely enjoying the social occasion. There were no public schools for girls in those days, but both Florence and her sister received an excellent education in the classics, modern languages, mathematics and literature, chiefly from their father. Florence was the more apt pupil. Even by modern standards they both received an excellent education.

From early years Florence evinced a desire to do something useful in the world. When she was seventeen she underwent a mental crisis. In later life she often referred to this as the day on which 'God called her to His service.' She then received the conviction that there was important work for her to do. From time to time she visited and helped to nurse the sick poor, and she gradually came to believe that nursing was her mission in life. In 1844, when she was twenty-four years old, she asked a visitor from America, Dr Howe, if it would be a dreadful thing for her to take up nursing, and he replied encouragingly, 'It would be unusual, and in England whatever is unusual is thought to be unsuitable, but I say to

you "go forward" if you have a vocation for that way of life.'
Florence thereupon made up her mind to obtain training in nursing
at a hospital, but when she broached the matter with her mother
and sister they were furious with her, and even her father, a
sympathetic but weak-willed man, was disgusted. Florence was
terribly disappointed, and wrote in her diary—

> Thou, O Lord, who knowest all things, I do not think Thou wilt
> insist upon my taking up life again—Thou seest that I can make
> nothing of it. If, as papa says, this is vanity and selfishness then Lord,
> all is wrong and there will be nothing of me left—my inmost self
> is hollow. Wilt thou not, O Lord, call the spirit of life back to thyself
> and send it out again under a new form, for if memory is left there
> will be no heaven for me—if the present is remembered in anything . . .

That was the cry of agony, of a distraught mind. Yet there was a
saving grace of common sense within her which was revealed in a
note a month later.

> Oh, if one has but a toothache what remedies are invented, what
> carriages, horses, ponies, journeys, doctors, chaperones are urged
> upon us, but if it is something to do with the mind, unless it belongs
> to one of the three heads, loss of friends, loss of fortune or loss of
> health, it is neither believed nor understood, and every different kind
> of suffering is ranged under the comprehensive word 'fancy,' and
> disposed of within one comprehensive remedy, concealment or
> self-communion, which is the same thing.

Remarkable psychological insight is revealed in that passage. A
few days later she wrote again—

> God has something for me to do for Him or He would have let me
> die some time ago. I hope to do it by living—then my eyes would
> indeed have seen his salvation.

The emotional conflict continued, but the patient found some
relief by rising early, and unknown to her family, studying everything she could get hold of relating to hospitals. It was during this
time that she laid up in her amazingly retentive memory that
store of information which was later to make her the best-informed
person in Europe about the structure and administration of hospitals. Whenever an opportunity offered, she inspected hospitals
and learnt their method of administration.

In 1846 Chevalier Bunsen (who knew and sympathized with her desire to do some useful work) sent her the Yearbook of the Institute of Deaconesses at Kaiserswerth. She read this and made up her mind to go thither to train as a nurse. In October 1846 she wrote—

When I want Erfrischung I read a little of the Jahresberichte über die Diakonissen Anstalt in Kaiserswerth. There is my home: there are my brothers and sisters all at work. There my heart is and there, I trust, one day will be my body, whether in this state or in the next, in Germany or in England. I do not care.

Her continued frustration was obviously leading to a breakdown in health, but a welcome interlude of a visit to Rome in 1847 brought her some relief. It was in Rome that she met Sidney Herbert and Lord Shaftesbury, two kindred spirits, and the artistic associations of the ancient city enriched her life. Yet her intention to do nursing remained inflexible in spite of the determined opposition of her family.

In 1849 a further crisis occurred. Richard Moncton Milnes (afterwards Lord Houghton) asked her to marry him. She admired him and had a great affection for him, but she rejected his proposal because she knew, or thought she knew, that he could not wholly sympathize with her moral aspirations and life-work. It was a calculated decision which caused her much mental agony and it further depressed her spirit. When in 1850 she went with friends on a visit to Egypt the entries in her diary show that she was on the verge of a mental breakdown. On the way back she called at Kaiserswerth and renewed her determination to go there for training.

On Christmas Eve in 1850 she wrote in her diary an account of her feelings which gives the reader some idea of the terrible crisis which this devoted woman experienced and the mental shock she suffered.

My God, what is to become of me? It is now, a year and a half since hope rose high and my great effort was made to crucify the old Flo, and, breaking through the old habits entailed upon me by an idle life, of living not in the present world of action, but in a future one of dreams to die and live again. That effort failed—what laws I had not observed in making it I have not yet discovered. In my thirty first year I can see nothing desirable but death. Entire change of air, Lord, thou knowest my heart, I cannot understand it. I am ashamed to understand it.

I know that if I were to see him again, the very thought of doing so overcomes me. I know that since I refused him not one day has passed without my thinking of him, that life is desolate to me to the last degree without his sympathy—and yet do I wish to marry him? I know that I could not bear the life—that to be nailed to a continuation and exaggeration of my present life without hope of another would be intolerable to me—that voluntarily to put it out of my power ever to seize the chance of forming for myself a true and rich life would seem to me like suicide—and yet my present life is suicide.

Determination was overcoming the resistance, but at a cost. In 1851, in spite of the almost maniacal opposition of her sister and the equally unsympathetic attitude of her mother, she went to stay at Kaiserswerth for three months. As she said good-bye to her sister, who, though furious, had accompanied her to Kaiserswerth, Florence, about to enter the training school, generously offered her bracelets to her sister to wear. Instead of welcoming the gift, Parthenope in anger flung the bracelets in the face of her sister. On this incident Florence later commented in her diary, 'the scene which followed was so violent that I fainted.' More significant was the entry which she wrote but crossed out with a stroke of the pen:'then first felt the symptoms of disease which is now slowly bringing me to my grave.' Clearly the anger of her sister Parthenope raised such an emotional storm that it showed itself in a visible physical reaction.

When Miss Nightingale returned from Kaiserswerth her sister made one more attempt to subdue her, this time by insisting that she (Parthenope) was so ill that she needed the constant attention of Florence. But Florence was now seeing and thinking more clearly. As Mrs Woodham Smith so justly says: 'That summer her attitude to life began to change—she began to realize that she must act.'

Sir James Clark told Florence that her sister must be taught to

live alone without her ministrations. During the next eighteen
months Florence spent a considerable time away from home and
began to act more independently. She was still convinced that
she had a mission in life; in June 1852 she affirmed this conviction—

> I have been brought hither by the laws of God—the circumstances
> acting upon the nature it was impossible that I should feel otherwise
> than I do.—I shall be brought through by the laws of God.

The decisive break-away from her family took place in April 1853
when she took the post of superintendent of nursing at the small
hospital in Harley Street. Here, immersed in problems of practical
nursing, she rapidly developed her remarkable but hitherto latent
powers of administration. She felt independent of her family and
did not encourage visits from her sister, who, according to Florence,
used to have hysterical attacks whenever she visited the hospital.
This experience gave her confidence in her own powers, so that
when the call to the Crimea came, she was ready for the task.

The sudden introduction of this delicately nurtured lady into the
overcrowded hospitals filled with terribly wounded and mortally
sick men, coupled with the difficulties of administering the female
nursing, arranging special diets, keeping records of the large sums
of money entrusted to her, and trying to overcome the veiled and
sometimes open opposition to her work, taxed her strength to
the utmost. Her friends and companions marvelled at her staying
power.

But action and reaction are equal and opposite, and when she
came back to England she was pale, weak, thin, and physically at a
low ebb. Her spirit was still burning brightly and her resolution
did not falter. Her purpose of improving the sanitary conditions in
the Army, and of making the Medical Service more effective,
sustained her. How she initiated this great movement during 1856
and 1857 is well known. During this period she worked all day
and often part of the night, took no holiday, ate little, slept badly,
lost weight and became irritable. Anything or anybody which
prevented or hindered her working exasperated her. She did not
welcome her relatives, and on 10 August 1857, after she and Dr
Sutherland had with feverish haste completed the report of the

Sanitary Commission, she physically collapsed and could do no more. She went to Malvern, where she could be alone and take the 'water-cure.' The doctor found that her heart was palpitating and beating rapidly. He told her that she must lie down and not get up till her heart had become normal. From that time to the end of her life—fifty-three years—she lived on a couch or in a wheel-chair.

When she returned to London the expectation of a visit from her sister was sufficient to bring on an attack of palpitation, rapid breathing, headache, and pain in the heart region. Her sister put off her visit. For some time the prospect of any unpleasant occurrence, an unwanted visit, or even opposition to her wishes or non-agreement with her opinions, was sufficient to bring on an attack. She was thus prevented from doing anything she did not want to do, or from meeting anyone whom she disliked. Thus was formed the habit of life which became confirmed and continued long after the immediate crisis was past. She concentrated on her work, had no desire for anything else other than the big schemes which occupied all her waking hours.

Miss Nightingale was not paralysed. No one has ever stated that she suffered from any organic disease. If she travelled (as she did infrequently) she would have a special railway carriage, but she seldom moved from South Street. She began to take a morbid pleasure in speaking about her weakness and her severe pain, which however did not prevent her working hard.

In a letter to Dr Pattison Walker in 1865 she wrote—

There is nothing, really nothing on this side of the grave which I long for so much as a visit to India—nothing which would interest me so much. But alas for me, it is quite impossible. I shall never leave London except for the grave. Even the move to the next street brings me to death's door. And I am assured that I have no prospect except of getting worse though it appears that I must have a (family) constitution like iron, for, for nearly seven years I have never been expected to live 6 months.

Three years later she wrote again to the same doctor in a similar strain.

Her invalidity did not curb her intellectual activity, nor did it impede her voluminous correspondence, but she got into the habit of ending her letters with a complaint of her illness or weakness. In January 1880 she wrote: 'but for six years and a month (since my dear father's death) I have never had one day's rest of body or mind.' In August 1888 she wrote to nurse Rees: 'I have been five months ill and only five times up and much overworked.'

Though she almost boasted of her weakness, she must actually have had great staying power, and this she herself realized. In a letter written to Mr Devine in August 1890, when she was seventy years old, she said—

I trust to your kindness to forgive an overworked invalid for not having answered you sooner.—for the last 40 years I have been immersed in two objects and have undertaken what might well occupy 20 vigorous young people—and I am an old and overworked invalid.

Old and overworked—yes, but invalid, physically invalid, hardly. From 1890 onwards Miss Nightingale's activities gradually lessened, she became stouter, less severe, but she retained her invalid state.

We are now in a position to consider what was the true nature of Miss Nightingale's invalidity. She had no serious organic disease. As she said, she had an iron constitution which enabled her to write voluminously—and writing is a tiring occupation.

Both Miss Nightingale and her sister Parthenope were what is commonly called 'highly strung' and very emotional. Parthenope was at times hysterical, and Florence was liable to fits of depression. For almost ten years she eagerly desired to be a nurse, but was frustrated by her family. She was torn between duty to her family and eagerness to obey what she regarded as a divine call. The emotional conflict which was intensified by her renunciation of marriage, began to be resolved when she began nursing. Then came the Crimean episode, with its terrible overwork and anxiety, with illness and physical exhaustion. On her return from the Crimea she took no rest and made no public appearance but immediately plunged into the campaign for Army Medical reform.

At this task she worked with almost superhuman energy, but when the report was finished she collapsed and was compelled to rest at Malvern. When she returned to town she had already adopted the state of an invalid, and any unpleasant prospect brought on 'attacks' of palpitation, etc.

Everyone knows that the mind has a great influence over the body. Pleasure or pain, fear or sudden anxiety, may cause the cheek to blush or blanch, may cause the heart to beat too fast or to miss a beat, may cause pain in the abdomen or even in other parts of the body. Everyone knows also that when a person is extremely fatigued they are more susceptible to annoying influences. At the time of Florence Nightingale's breakdown she was exhausted by three years' experiences which would have taxed the strength of the strongest, and prior to that she had been the victim of an emotional conflict which, to a person of her sensibility, must have been of terrible intensity. It was more than a normal person could be expected to bear. No wonder that her nervous system reacted on her body and that she developed what is commonly called a neurosis, for that is the correct term to apply to her condition.

This type of neurosis is frequently only a temporary event and the patient often recovers completely. Such disorders with subsequent recovery were common in the First World War, when a neurosis sometimes termed 'disordered action of the heart' led to the invaliding of many soldiers. Why then did not recovery follow in the case of Florence Nightingale?

There is no simple answer to this question. If Miss Nightingale had been an ordinary person it is likely that she might in time have resumed something like the life of a normal person. But she was not an ordinary person, nor did she wish to live the life of an ordinary person. Social activities, holidays, travel, entertainments, convivial meetings, were to her frivolities compared with her great, what she considered her divine, mission in life. This she found she could do as well in seclusion as anywhere else. She hated publicity, though undoubtedly she loved power. She disliked company, except such as would help her in her work. She found that her invalid state enabled her the more easily to induce those whom she wished to interview—statesmen, generals, viceroys, distinguished doctors, nurses—to come to see her at her own time under the most convenient conditions. Much of her work was secret, and secrets are better kept in seclusion. Moreover, those who were opposed to her did not feel justified in openly opposing an invalid.

Though it would be wrong to say and unfair to think that Miss Nightingale ever consciously took advantage of her invalidity, it is certain that it was in some respects advantageous to her attaining the objects which she had at heart. It is probably true to say that she was able to achieve more by withdrawing herself from the world than she would have done if she had partaken of the ordinary social activities. In some respects her invalidity resembled that of Miss Barrett before Robert Browning appeared on the scene. Miss Barrett's seclusion gave her more time to write beautiful poetry, but she recovered her full normal activities under the stimulus of a great passion. Miss Nightingale had sacrificed her love to her career, or rather to the fulfilment of her great mission. It was a noble sacrifice.

Index